# BLACK | RED
# HORSE | DOG

*'In fact,'* Hot Horse Herbie *says, 'if it does not win,*
*you can never speak to me again.'*
*'Well,' I say, as I start to walk away,*
*'I am not interested in any tip at this time.'*
*'Now,' Herbie says, 'wait a minute. A story goes with it.'*
*'Well,' I say, coming back to him, 'let me hear the story.'*

DAMON RUNYON
A Story Goes With It

# BLACK | RED
# HORSE | DOG

## ...MORE GAMBLING YARNS

### MICHAEL CHURCH

# DEDICATION

*Black Horse – Red Dog* is dedicated to my wife Pat, who devoted many hours to helping me write these stories.

Published in 2008 by Highdown,
an imprint of Raceform Ltd
Compton, Newbury, Berkshire, RG20 6NL

A CIP catalogue record for this book is available from the British Library.

ISBN 978-1-905156-51-1

Cover designed by Phil Brown
Interiors designed by Fiona Pike

Printed in the UK by CPI Williams Clowes Beccles NR34 7TL

# BY THE SAME AUTHOR

*Three Centuries of Leading Sires 1721-1987*
*The Classic Pedigree 1776-1989*
*Dams of Classic Winners 1777-1993*
*The Derby Stakes 1780-1997*
*Eclipse – The Horse – The Race – The Awards*
*Ripping Gambling Yarns – Tales of a misspent youth*
*Born to Bet – Further tales of a misspent youth*
*Champion Sires 1722-2003*
*Classic Pedigrees 1776-2005*
*The Derby Stakes – The Complete History – 1780-2006*

Also a series of pedigree charts including:
*The Derby Chart 1780-2007*
*The Two Thousand Guineas Chart 1809-1985*
*The Magnificent Seven Classic Winners*
*The Godolphin Group 1 Winners Charts*

# CONTENTS

# ACKNOWLEDGEMENTS

At Raceform, I should like to thank Julian Brown and James de Wesselow for their confidence and support in this project. I am also grateful to Fiona Pike for the interior layouts and to John Hopkins for the proofreading. Once again, Phil Brown of Thoroughbred Advertising has produced an exciting and creative front cover, the images on which are accredited to Gilbert Holiday.

All the pictures in this book were provided by the Church family. However, whilst every effort has been made to trace the copyright holders of the illustrations, this has not been possible in every case. The publishers will therefore be pleased to rectify any omissions whenever possible.

# LIST OF ILLUSTRATIONS

# FOREWORD

Welcome to his world. Michael Church may look respectable, maybe a bit clerkish, on the outside, but it's clear from these stories that he actually lives in a parallel universe.

It's a rare and captivating place set initially in the grey, smoke-filled days of Woking in the late 1940s when the rent was £3 a week which was made into a small fortune after Uncle Albert lumped two week's worth on the Queen's horse Manicou at Kempton on Boxing Day.

We follow Michael's betting wiles from 'Big Al' in schoolboy boxing, to the moustachioed Flt Lt Ruggles and Aircraftsman Church in Bristol, and on to the tale of Maggie and the Queen of Diamonds on the train back from Cheltenham.

We even skip back a couple of generations to the 1919 Derby and somebody called 'Princess Katrina – Star of The East – Fortunes told for Sixpence'. What happens there is scarcely believable but that's just the point. You are in Michael's world. You are looking at it through his quirky glasses and you are always measuring whether there is better value than Damon Runyon's oft- quoted 'all life is six to five against'.

In the racing world we go one better by saying that the game is a daily battle of hope against experience. Read these pages to find a good slice of both.

# INTRODUCTION

Whilst trying to think of a different angle for an introduction to this, my third book of short stories, the postman delivered a book for my wife Pat, who is a therapist. The book – *The Soul's Code* by James Hillman – lay on the dining room table for most of the day, until, intrigued by the title, I picked it up and read the first paragraph:

*'There is more in a human life than our theories of it allow. Sooner or later something seems to call us onto a particular path. You may remember this "something" as a signal moment in childhood when an urge out of nowhere, a fascination, a peculiar turn of events struck like an annunciation: This is what I must do, this is what I've got to have. This is who I am.'*

I was so impressed that I make no apology for recounting again my own particular awakening.

As a war-time evacuee from the age of four to nine, I returned home to Woking for our first family reunion on the Sunday before the 1945 Derby. Introduced to five of my dad's eight brothers, who seemed to be there solely to discuss the race, my life was changed irrevocably. All the talk was of the Derby. My impressions and senses were swamped by their enthusiasm and amid the smells of beer and

Woodbines, the names of Dante, Midas, Sun Storm, Harry Wragg and Gordon Richards took on a magical appeal.

I must have got very involved because I can remember Uncle Henry's lone voice trying to discourage me, saying it was a mug's game and that he had never backed a winner. But it was quite useless, for I took to racing like a duck to water.

The stories that follow are not only a dip into my past adventures, but also into those of my extended family – grandparents, aunts and uncles.

I hope the reader will enjoy these tales – oh, and to save the now elderly characters portrayed in these yarns from any sleepless nights, I have changed all their names. So let's begin without further ado.

# CHAPTER ONE

## *The School Olympics*

The last time the Olympic Games came to Britain, or to be precise London, was in 1948. And at that time, although I was regarded as a small boy, I was a regular both at horse and dog racing, and also attended professional football, boxing, speedway and ice hockey matches. Athletics, however, due to the distinct lack of betting opportunities, had never grabbed my attention.

Now, fuelled by the groundswell of interest generated by the Olympics, everyone I knew was talking about the popular athletes, MacDonald Bailey, Arthur Wint and, of course, Fanny Blankers-Koen. In fact, every playtime, class relay teams would hurtle their way round our playground, which invariably led to queues forming outside the first aid room for attention to grazed knees and elbows.

At this time, the School Sports loomed large in both teachers and pupil's consciousness. And although it had crossed my mind, that there might be some betting opportunities, it came as a major disappointment that the only events open to my age group, the 11- and 12-year-olds, were to be the egg and spoon, the three-legged race and the sack race. Who were the national heroes in those, I wondered?

I must have sulked for a week, until Uncle Ernie took the higher ground: 'Never mind about the betting lad, why don't you try and win something.'

Truth was, I was a moderate runner, unless someone was chasing me, and my lack of hand-to-eye coordination had cost me dearly at marbles, conkers and shove-ha'penny, so that ruled out the egg and spoon.

My thoughts turned to the sack race, until dad reminded me of my nightly struggle to remain upright whilst climbing into my pyjama trousers – so no go there.

Finally, I settled on the three-legged race, but as Uncle Ernie said, 'You'll have to find an agile partner for that one Michael.' He was right of course and by now I had started to give it serious thought.

The Goldsworth School 12-year-old mixed three-legged race, run over 50 yards, was for 16 boy/girl pairs, to be run in two heats of eight, the first four in each heat to run in the final. Uncle Ernie, having temporarily given up betting, was keen for me to run and to win, offering me a £1 note if I did, and he persuaded two of his brothers, Albert and Arthur, to stump up the same amount.

That was all very encouraging, but I still needed a partner. Many of my classmates thinking of entering were planning to run with their boy or girlfriends. So for me, inclined to be a loner, it narrowed the field considerably.

Meantime, using whatever was the 1940s equivalent of positive thinking, I started to consider the ideal type – a girl of the same height and build and, when I really thought about it, a left-footed girl. Her inside-right foot would be tethered to my inside-left foot, so each of us would be leading, in time, with our best foot on the outside, so driving forward our middle-peg.

The chosen object of my desire was Thelma. Bespectacled, she had freckles, a fringe and two short pigtails. But more relevantly, she had been a member of the junior school hockey team. So she was both well balanced, agile and the owner of a pair of satisfyingly sturdy legs.

After careful consideration, even at this young age, she would be a worthwhile ante-post bet for Council librarian. On the other hand, if she later chose to smoke and drink, she would be nailed on for the cast of St Trinian's.

For someone who I had hardly spoken to before, when approached she was surprisingly compliant with my wishes.

The following school lunch break, after adopting a straight-back stance and clasping each other firmly around the waist, we set off in a series of short sprints, up and down, in front of the bicycle sheds.

As we progressed in our training, we began to feel our elevation from 'bus horses' to thoroughbreds. This new image was further supported by Thelma's excellent suggestion that we breathe in unison. At this point, I began to congratulate myself on my inspired choice of partner.

Since playtime was not primarily designed for practising the egg and spoon race – no spare eggs in 1948 – or the sack race – most spare sacks having vanished to reappear on parents' allotments filled with potatoes – by comparison, the three-legged race seemed ideal. And, when a teachers committee gave permission for prospective entrants to practise in the girls playground, a hitherto gentile hideaway, it took on the appearance of the chariot races run in the Coliseum.

Meanwhile, once again, my reputation had gone before me and I was summoned for questioning by Headmaster 'Bonk' Peel, to be warned of the consequences of betting.

Marshalling me into his study, he began, 'Church, you are not going to turn our 'Olympic sports day' into a disreputable occasion are you?'

He sat menacingly on the end of his desk, glowering at me with knitted eyebrows.

'You remember what happened on our last encounter, when we confiscated your double-headed penny?'

I did indeed, and to reinforce his threat he took one of the five switches from behind his desk, momentarily trying them out for flexibility.

'I w-wouldn't dream of it Sir,' I said with a slight tremble.

He looked past me, my reply having no impact on his impending lecture.

'By that, I mean no wagering; not sixpences, thrupences or even pennies. Do you understand Church?' he said, swishing the cane in the metre of his threat. Fully wound up he continued, 'The Olympics are a proud occasion for everyone in the British Isles. Remember Church, it's not about winning, but taking part – right Church?'

'Right Sir. Permission to speak Sir?'

'Yes Church.'

'W-well, to say as yet, I haven't taken a single bet.'

'As yet, as yet!' Peel fumed.

'Well Sir, I m-meant to add – and I don't intend to.'

'I should hope not. Is that a promise Church? You know the consequences.'

'Alright then, a promise,' I said, resolutely.

Bonk kept up his frown, but I did hear his secretary, who had crept in midway through his tirade, give a sigh of relief.

Sports day arrived and although the older boys and girls were talking about the hurdles, long jump and discus – the javelin had been passed over as an accident waiting to happen – to the first and second years the games were all about eggs, sacks and three legs.

At that morning's assembly, Bonk Peel, not feeling the need for diplomacy, announced that the sports day would open with three 'novelty events' for the first and second years. Immediately afterwards, Billy Barker, who later in life worked for a racecourse bookmaker, on hearing of my solemn pledge to Bonk, seized the opportunity to price up all three events.

The egg and spoon was first up. Ten went to post in one heat over 35 yards, girls receiving five yards.

Known at school as the 'conker kings', Alfie Parker and Peter Hapgood quickly approached Barker for prices on both little Sammy Marsh and Penelope King. And, as neither were thought to have a serious chance, Barker laid them 12-1 against each to the tune of two half-crowns each-way. Despite the strength of the bets, Barker felt they were tinged with sentiment, Marsh being little more than an errand boy for their shady dealings and Hapgood openly declaring a soft spot for Penny.

Oh, I forgot to tell you that Hapgood's mother kept chickens and was to supply the fresh eggs for the competition.

Off and running, the bigger boys set the pace, but strangely, around the 25-yard mark, most of the front-runners' eggs rolled off their spoons when faced with a head-on wind. Meanwhile, Sammy King, barely four foot tall, and the pretty Penelope picked their way through the chaotic scenes of fallen eggs and outbursts of 'bugger and sod it' from the first form intake.

Some thought Penelope would have won, but for a sideways glance and wink at Peter, enough for little Sammy to get up in the final yards to win by a short arm.

There was great applause from Peter and Alfie and, even greater restraint, as they withheld their rush for payment until a less conspicuous moment.

Due to the chaos, an announcement of a 'stewards enquiry' called for Miss Sims (domestic science) to examine the eggs. However, her wisdom in giving the all clear after testing the eggs of the winner and runner-up was sadly misplaced, as later that afternoon, spectators who had the misfortune to tread on the discarded eggs of the losers, noticed their lack of yoke – half the contents having been blown out by a straw! Strangely, all this caused little concern, unlike Headmaster Peel's reference to the early events as 'novelty'.

'We'll give him bloody novelty, if he wants novelty,' fumed Colin Nixon and Janet O'Brien, both of whom had been given double homework for coming back late from playtime after practising their three-legged technique.

And, as their resentment passed from pupil to pupil, so plans of sabotage began to be hatched; Janet and Colin, who enjoyed a bit of anarchy, nipped out to buy five pounds of over-ripe tomatoes to drop in the bottom of some of the sacks. But the most outrageous story going around was that Alfie Parker, whose father was a builder, had been seen knocking up half-a-yard of quick-setting cement at the back of the bicycle sheds.

As the competitors waited for the sack race, Hapgood and Parker played their part in the subterfuge, offering their services to give out the sacks and get the runners on their starting positions. Artmaster Norman, who was responsible for this task, welcomed their offer, being only too pleased to have some assistance.

Although always under Bonk's careful gaze, I was in this case 'pure as the driven', but if the rumours were anything to go by, I thought it best to view the race away from those marshalling it.

'Sackracers get ready,' boomed Norman through his hand-held megaphone, 'Set – Go!'

Ten bobbing 11-year-olds bounced up and down in line for about 20 yards, before suddenly, Tommy Smith seemed to skid uncontrollably into Rosie Higgins, bringing her down and two others close behind.

The situation reminded me of Becher's Brook in those early Grand National newsreels. Worse was to come when two other boys collided near the line, sliding off into the parents' deckchairs and scattering tea and biscuits in all directions.

Throughout this gentile mayhem, Janet, Colin and their friends could be seen falling to the ground, helpless with laughter at the success of their dubious intervention.

Four did eventually finish, but such was the noise and distraction that only the participants and one or two of the teacher's thought there may have been foul play afoot.

Even when Freddie Phillips went up to collect his book token prize, and noticed squashed tomatoes on the soles of his plimsolls, he didn't think to report it. Bonk, meanwhile, had gone over to Artmaster Norman to find the reason for so many fallers. Norman, with an air of great concern, said he would look into all the empty sacks, but by then the Machiavellian pair Hapgood and Parker had done away with the evidence.

The three-legged race was next up, and for Thelma and I, this had all the importance of the Cheltenham Gold Cup. But despite being sorely tempted, I stayed true to my promise to Bonk and turned a deaf ear to Barker's shout of, 'Four to One the field for the three-legged.'

This was by far the most competitive of the three 'novelty' events with 32 runners – 16 pairs – to run in two heats of eight. There were no lanes in this event as the width of the start exceeded the usual boundaries.

I must admit that Thelma and I were nervous; we had put so much thought into our training. I looked around me at the start, keeping a watchful eye on Hapgood and Parker, just in case something was afoot.

'On your marks – Set – Go!'

We jumped off leading with our outside legs whilst holding each other's waist tight. Drawn in the middle, we encountered bits of bumping; one girl's shoe came off and another couple's leg-tie came undone. But we kept going to finish second, four yards behind Colin and Janet.

We didn't stay to watch the second heat, preferring instead to go behind the cricket pavilion and, after taking off the silk scarf that bound our legs we lay flat out on the grass and relaxed. We had made the final!

Ten minutes later, we were tracked down by Thelma's anxious parents.

'There you are. What are you doing down there?' they echoed.

But I could see the relief on her mother's face, when she saw we were rubbing the embrocation into our own thighs rather than each other's!

Mr Norman's megaphone called us to the start for the three-legged final. Eight pairs lined up, we were drawn six, Colin and Janet seven.

'Ready – Set – Go!' We bounded from the line in unison, for once the whole seeming greater than the sum of the parts. We were flying and at halfway we led by about two yards. Then, in an effort to storm up our outside, Colin clipped the heel of Thelma, causing her head to go back, then violently forward, sending her glasses flying into our path. I heard the crunch beneath us – it was sickening.

Although Thelma swore and momentarily checked her stride, she kept going with a grim determination – a girl after my own heart.

By now, however, Colin and Janet had taken the lead, but we gave chase, and after a tremendous tussle, joined them right on the line.

After an endless wait for the result, during which Mr Norman consulted three parent judges, he finally announced, 'After a split decision from our three judges, the result, of a close and dramatic final, goes to … Colin Nixon and Janet O'Brien.'

Cue some wild cheering from their friends and firm clapping, led by Norman, Bonk and two of the three-strong panel of parent judges.

Thelma and I stood there for a moment in shock, waiting for our minds to catch up with the reality of our disappointment. Shortly, Thelma's parents swarmed upon us with, 'What bad luck dear. Did you think you'd won? Thelma, where are your glasses?' None of which either of us attempted to answer. And from that moment on, after what had seemed to us as a personal tragedy, our friendship steadily grew.

That evening, Thelma's parents invited me round for tea, and to give them credit, they never mentioned the likely cost of new glasses once. Over cream buns and strawberry jam, I realised how lucky I had been to find a girl as committed and obsessional as myself, one in whose company I now no longer stammered.

In the very happy months that followed, whilst guiding her gently through what was for her the uncharted waters of fixed odds football pools, we became an item, both in the classroom, sitting next to each other for algebra, and out of it, standing behind the goal at Woking.

Twenty years later, at Sir Ivor's Derby, I thought I saw her in the grandstand. The pigtails had gone, but she still had the glasses and the freckles. I tried to get a closer look, but suddenly, she became engulfed in the crowd, and I could never be sure.

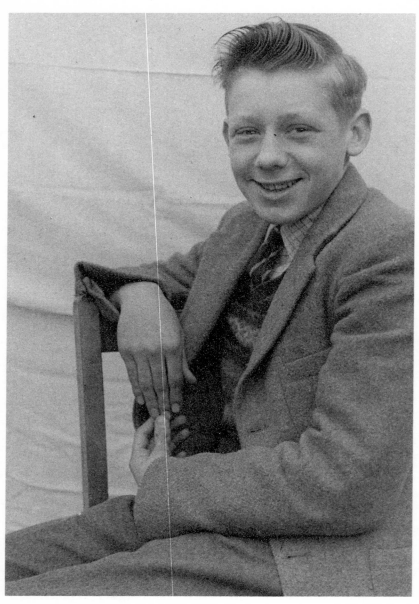

*The young Michael*

# CHAPTER TWO

## *Auntie Mary and a Royal Occasion*

Christmas Day was always kept at home with the family; mum, dad, nan, Judy the dog and me. With similar regularity, on Boxing Day, we walked from our little bungalow in Clarence Avenue, to Auntie Mary's terraced house in Church Street, a distance of 500 yards exactly.

I was quite sure of that, having regularly paced the journey to visit my cousin Peter on Sunday mornings. And, significant to me, a 14-year-old boy on the slippery slope, as the standard distance at Wimbledon dog track.

Greeted at the door of 199 by Mary, Henry and Peter, we were shown to their front room. It was a welcoming sight, with its colourful paper chains, large paper bells, sprigs of holly and a small artificial tree covered in lights.

'Henry fixed the lights just an hour ago,' Mary said joyfully.

'One of the bulbs had worked loose, but we didn't know which one!' she added, her voice booming with the sense of occasion.

To cross the room, however, was in truth, akin to crossing a minefield, for another of dad's brothers, Albert – who owned the property and rented it to Henry – had done nothing to repair the dry rot that lurked perilously beneath the freshly hoovered carpet.

'Mind how you go Stan,' Mary cautioned, shepherding in dad like the usherette she once was.

'The seat over by the fireplace is quite safe, and Dorothy, if you sit on the settee with me.' Then in a hushed and dignified tone, she added, 'We put two large metal trays under the casters to save us falling through.'

Warming to her roll as hostess, Mary directed, 'Oh Henry, go into the kitchen and get us all a cup of tea and a mince pie, and nan, there's a wicker chair for you under the radio.'

Peter and I, a little squeezed for room, were told to play in the kitchen. 'You know, the game you like to play on Sunday mornings,' Mary continued, tirelessly, 'guessing the football crowds in the paper, I've saved last Sunday's *News of the World* 'specially for you.'

Hardly a school certificate subject, but perhaps it should have been, since we both excelled at it. Anyway, true to form, Mary had put up a child's see-through Christmas stocking as a prize for the winner – the ones with chocolate money, sugar mice and those tiny packs of playing cards with Scotty dogs on the back. Oh, and those small tin scales to weigh sweets on. Not much for a 14-year-old boy you might say, but then Mary called out from the front room that she had included *Old Moore's Almanack*.

'It usually gives some veiled hints for next year's Derby and Grand National. And somewhere in there,' she enthused, 'there's trap numbers to back in reversed forecasts for all the London dog tracks!'

An hour later, I was enjoying a thumb through *Old Moore's*, a little guiltily I must confess, since it had fallen to me to guess the Blackpool home crowd, which as every schoolboy knew, was invariably a capacity 30,000. Like taking a penalty kick really.

Anyway, Henry topped us up with more tea and mince pies on yet another tin tray – *The Laughing Cavalier* this time. If there was one thing Auntie Mary had in spades it was tin trays – multi-purposed in her house!

*Little Peter*

Meanwhile, spirits were high in the front room, with Mary telling mum how her friend Phyllis, had, during the war, seen the King and Queen inspecting the bomb damage in the East End of London.

'They were very friendly, Phyllis told me, and she gave me the cuttings out of her *News Chronicle* – for my Royal scrapbooks you know.'

Auntie Mary was a devout Royalist; she had dozens of these scrapbooks, allegedly, full of Royal births, deaths and marriages, even pictures of past Royal Ascots – so she said.

However, mysteriously, as yet we had never seen any of them, and, despite our enthusiasm, we didn't see them today either.

Suddenly, there was a knock at the door. Mary, peering round the aspidistra and, slightly twitching the net curtain, said 'Bloody hell it's Albert, surely he hasn't come for the rent on Boxing Day?'

Albert entered with his usual cocky smile, producing from behind his back with a flourish a bag containing a bottle of Sandiman's port, a Christmas pudding laced with brandy and a wrapper containing 200 Craven A ciggies, the ones with the black cat on the box – the latter a life or death line for Mary and Henry. Then, going back to his fish van, parked across the road, he returned with an oblong wooden box – in it was a top grade Scottish salmon. 'A rarity, even among the gentry,' said Albert with another broad grin. And, no, he hadn't forgotten Peter either, who, disappearing into the scullery with a brown paper parcel, joyfully unwrapped a bright new red and white Woking football scarf.

Mary seemed a little flummoxed at Albert's sudden generosity and for once, untypically, steered him clear of the dangerous carpet zones. In the meantime, my dad, oblivious to the latest turn of events, inevitably redirected the conversation to Woking's recent 3-0 victory over Wimbledon. 'Alfie Welland scored two and ...' his account was suddenly interrupted by cheers of relief at Peter's perfectly timed entrance in his pristine scarf.

Mary, meanwhile, was disappearing upstairs, when Albert, anxiously fearing that the weight of the gathering might prove costly, nervously called after her, 'I can't stay Mary, I'm just going to pick up Charlie; we're going to Kempton.'

Mary returned, slightly out of breath, to ask in a confidential whisper, 'Do you know anything good?'

'Well, Charlie says the Queen's got Manicou in the King George and, it's a live'un!'

Mary thrust a small white envelope into Albert's hand, 'Two weeks rent, Albert. Sorry for the delay, but it's Christmas yer know.' She followed him out to the van.

'You're a real brick Mary,' Albert said earnestly, turning to meet her face on, 'That's very much appreciated,' he said with a wink, 'It'll make my day!'

Mary started to hop from one foot to the other, like a little girl.

'Albert, that Queen's horse Manna-something or other, would you put a bit on for me?' Albert nodded and with that, she slipped something into his overcoat pocket.

'Must fly now Mary,' said Albert. 'Enjoy the salmon,' and with that, his fish van disappeared round the corner and out of sight.


Kempton was cold, bright and sunny and, there was a feeling of optimism amongst the packed crowd. The first three favourites had all gone in and now the seven runners for the King George were making their way to post.

Albert, who had the questionable system of backing horses with the initial letters of A, C, and E in a treble, had already landed the first two legs with Easy Winner and Attentif, and was now sweating on Coloured School Boy in the big'un.

Just as the field came into line Albert remembered Mary's bet and, thrusting his hand into his overcoat pocket, rushed up to Stringer's joint in the front row and pushed the bet into his hand, shouting out, 'Manicou, on the nose.'

There were no big screens, or even commentaries on racecourses in 1950, so binoculars of all shapes and sizes were trained up the home straight. First round the final bend was the blue; buff stripes, blue sleeves and black cap of Queen Elizabeth's Manicou, who, although joined two out by Silver Fame (ridden by the future crime writer, Dick Francis), drew away to win by three lengths.

*Uncle Albert and the fish van*

After the race, Uncles Charlie and Albert met up in front of the bookies. Charlie had collected a nice touch, while typically, Albert, having stayed faithful to his ACE system, had nothing to collect from third placed Coloured School Boy. Then, almost as an afterthought, he remembered Mary's bet on Manicou, and rummaging in his pocket for the ticket, gave it to Charlie to collect.

Returning a few minutes later, with an expression of veiled incredulity, Charlie enquired cautiously, 'How much did Mary have on that Queen's horse?'

'Don't know, exactly,' Albert said. 'Stringer did say, but we were both in such a hurry I didn't catch it. She had it wrapped up in an envelope.'

His hand slid back into his pocket and as it did, so Albert's expression changed. Pulling out another envelope, he opened it – a ten bob note!

Mary's two weeks' rent had amounted to £6 and now, at 5-1 ...

'Blimey, I've put the rent money on,' Albert exclaimed, his conscience

suddenly working overtime with the thoughts of, 'If only I had collected the bet myself.'

Albert thrust out his hand to Charlie. 'Give me the money, I'll deduct the rent and pay Mary her winnings.'

'OK,' said Charlie, but knowing Albert of old, added, 'But won't Mary be delighted when I tell her she's won £30. I'm sure she'll forgive you the cock-up.'

Albert's face was a study; for once, he had been completely thwarted.

*Uncle Henry, Auntie Mary and Peter, later on Brighton Pier*

# CHAPTER THREE

## *Money for Jam*

'No Church, we don't want you to run a roulette wheel for the Autumn Fair.'

Headmaster 'Bonk' Peel made his feelings quite clear. Unfairly, I thought, since the proceeds from my running a Crown & Anchor dice game the previous year had exceeded the returns from all the other stalls put together.

The reason for his firm stance, I eventually gleaned from Ma Snow, our elderly, slightly built and deeply religious English teacher.

'I'm in complete agreement with our headmaster; you cannot have school finances being funded by illegal gambling,' she continued, her voice quavering a little. 'I'll tell you something to ponder Church; you might be Bill Long's (the head math teacher) blue-eyed boy, but, to the rest of the staff you are a constant cause of concern – corrupting your classmates with gambling and bringing the school into disrepute on numerous sports days.'

'Come on Miss, that's a bit strong in'it?'

But before she could reply, our conversation was interrupted by the lunchtime bell – time for me to price up a couple of handicaps at Sandown for my fellow fifth-formers.

The following morning, Bonk closed the school assembly with news that, 'To encourage greater involvement, this year (1952), the Autumn Fair will have three new competitions for pupils only – the best Victoria sponge; the finest home-made jam and the most beautiful flower arrangement.'

It seemed there would be prizes for the first three in each category, thereafter all the entries would be sold for the benefit of school funds – great! It all sounded very dull and, as usual, Bonk's idea of greater involvement looked certain to fall on deaf ears.

But, hold on, I could see a glimmer of hope.

Supposin', there were, say, two dozen entries in each category; the prizes would almost certainly be book tokens, they usually were. Perhaps pupils might welcome the chance to pick a winner – win or each way, at 10-1 the field? I was warming to the idea by the minute. I might even enter the Jam competition myself, after all, my nan, Alicia Margaret, once won a prize for her home-made marmalade.

Two weeks before the Autumn Fair, lists were put up on the notice board for entries to the new competitions.

Billy Barker was first to read my mind.

'Goin' to make a book on Bonk's Triple Crown?'

'If there's goin' to be enough entries,' I replied guardedly.

'Course there will be,' he enthused. 'Look there's eight down for the cake making already.'

'Sounds promising then,' I said with a grin.

Having been assured that marmalade qualified as jam, that evening, I told nan of the competition and asked if she could help me with her secret recipe.

'You get the oranges, say a dozen and two lemons. That should be enough for three pounds of marmalade. When you've got those, I'll show you.'

We scrubbed the oranges, cut them in half and juiced them. We then scraped out the insides and cut up the outer skin in fine slices for the rind. Then we did the same with the lemons and added the lemon juice to that of the oranges.

Nan then rolled up her sleeves. She was in her element again, pouring the juice into measuring jars, finding a muslin bag for the rinds, putting everything back into the saucepan, with water and three cupfuls of sugar.

It was beginning to smell now, and it smelt lovely.

Thirty minutes later, we were ladling out the mixture into jars and putting on the lids and rings.

'That should be good enough to win any competition,' nan said. 'We'll put the labels on tomorrow, when the marmalade has settled down.'

I felt I had learned a lot that day. Now I could discuss the making of marmalade and not just the odds on it!

Three days before the Autumn Fair, which by the way was to take place in the school hall at 2 p.m. on Wednesday, the entries for the three competitions had not lived up to early expectations – nine in the Victoria sponge, seven in the jams and only five in the flower arrangements.

The betting, which until then had been light, had suffered several revisions due to the lack of entries. And those who had made their choice from my opening prices of 10-1 the field, were now feeling very pleased with themselves.

But as so often happens in ante-post betting, the unexpected played a part. Once again Billy Barker was first to spot the seachange.

He told me that some of the older boys who liked a bet were planning to get their mums busy cake-baking, jam-making and cutting flowers from their gardens. Billy had also heard a rumour that Alfie Parker and Peter Hapgood – the conker kings – had a cunning plan to enter with two arrangements from their local florists, and their opening bets of five bob each-way on themselves led me to believe him.

Billy, however, was undeterred by the rumour and thrust a ten bob note in my hand.

'I'll take the 10-1 for that in the flower arrangin',' he said, nonchalantly.

Betting in the Jam Stakes had been slow until Colin Nixon and Janet O'Brien, winners of the three-legged race in an earlier story, were heard planning a jam assault by submitting jars of Rhubarb & Ginger.

I didn't know much about Victoria sponges, save the ones that mum made – 'Light as a feather,' dad would say, usually adding somewhat, negatively, 'nearly as nice as a shop sponge.'

So, on the principle of, 'If you can't beat them, join them,' mum's 'light as a feather' would run in the colours of Michael Church.

At around 2 p.m. parents and their friends started to drift into the hall. There were of course many things for them to spend their money on, such as trying to cover a half-crown with a penny by dropping it into a bucket of water – often tried, but rarely achieved.

The science master's game of running a circle-ended key along an electric wire without touching it proved popular with the dads, but the continuous buzzing noise was a particular source of pain to the other stall holders throughout the afternoon.

Other favourite sideshows were: *The Treasure Hunt, Name that Doll* and *Pin the Cigar on Winston Churchill* – three goes for a shilling – a bizarre alternative to the usual *Pin the Tail on the Donkey*.

The trestle tables showing the new competition entries drew considerable interest, and not only from the general public. An interesting spectacle was the judges doing their rounds, delicately tasting, lifting and viewing the entries, followed closely by a small group of dedicated punters avidly doing the same.

At 5 o'clock, Bonk rang the handbell and stood to one side of the stage.

'I am pleased to announce the results of the three new competitions,' he said as he smoothed back his silvered hair and adjusted his tie.

'After this announcement every entry on display may be purchased in aid of the school funds,' he laboured.

'First in the Victoria sponge,' he continued, 'is Annette Doubledown; second Valerie Shore and the third is a boy – Michael Church.'

'Very nice, very nice,' I said to myself, remembering that I had only taken a bob or two on Annette, despite her coming top in domestic science. And mum will be thrilled with third – I owe her a book token.

Bonk continued, this time with Ma Snow venturing up onto the stage to pass the magic envelope.

'The first prize for home-made jam goes to,' pause for dramatic effect, 'Janet O'Brien.'

'Sod it,' I mumbled.

I did so want nan to win with her marmalade.

'Second,' Bonk continued, 'goes to Wendy Thomas and third, to Colin Nixon.' He added: 'Both the first and third prizes were for the exotic Rhubarb and Ginger jam.'

But he wasn't finished yet. 'Oh and by the way, one entry was with marmalade, not strictly jam, but our panel thought the maker, Michael Church, deserved an honorary prize for a tasty entry.'

I was extremely miffed, since I was definitely told by the domestic science teacher that marmalade would be fine, but of course now she was nowhere to be found.

So far, on the betting front I had done really well, despite taking a knock from Janet and Colin's Rhubarb & Ginger, well supported at 6-1.

The flower arranging result would be crucial.

Bonk again took the stage, this time with a microphone brought in from the science room by Mr Faraday, intrusively, with 'Testing testing – 1, 2, 3, 4, 5.' He finally blew onto the mike and passed it over to the headmaster.

'Very competitive this class with 16 entries and some amazingly proficient – all for sale remember.'

He paused again as Ma Snow passed him the envelope with a nervous smile. Bonk opened it and looked surprised.

'All boys,' he exclaimed, with a puzzled expression. 'Admirable, admirable,' before continuing, 'First, Alfred Parker, second Peter Hapgood and third Billy Barker.'

A round of applause followed from the innocents, before Barker was seen approaching the stage.

Soon after, Bonk, Ma Snow and Billy Barker could be seen in an animated conversation – the three of them walking quickly over to the flower arrangement table. More arm-waving and astonishment from Ma Snow, before Bonk returned to the stage.

'We have, what I believe is called an objection to the winner and the second, by the third, Billy Barker.'

Bonk whipped his brow, and continued, his voice cracking occasionally with discomfort.

'After an examination of the first two arrangements, it is found that both were apparently assembled by *Wonder Blooms*, who had, unknown to our panel of judges, lodged their business cards within the flowers.

'The objection therefore, is sustained, and the first prize goes to Billy Barker. We thank you Billy for your observations.'

Talking to Billy afterwards, he triumphantly revealed to me that, in fact, all three bouquets were the work of Wonder Blooms. He alone, however, had the foresight to remove the evidence.

Secretly, I admired his initiative and wished I had thought of such a creative manoeuvre. In the run-up to next year's school sports day, I vowed to watch his bets very carefully.

*Nan and Michael –*
*the marmalade makers*

# CHAPTER FOUR

## *The Bruisers v The Booby*

A lan Rowbottom was one of those unfortunate boys who whatever he did and wherever he went, he was picked on and bullied. It started with his name, and then progressed to raw eggs broken into his gym shorts and soil shovelled into his socks.

When poor Alan's life reached an unbearable level, his anxious parents decided to change his school and enrol him in the local boxing club. His progress in a year surprised everyone, not least himself and he was featured with photographs in the local paper.

A big boy for his 15 years, he weighed 11 stone, with a face like baker's dough. However, after moving school and taking boxing lessons, he steadily gained confidence to win a series of amateur, three-round contests.

His parents, now leading lights in the local boxing club and proud of their son's achievements, had arranged with our headmaster, 'Bonk' Peel, to show the pupils of Goldsworth Secondary Modern School a boxing exhibition. The central purpose of this edifying entertainment was to include two two-round contests, with a suitable interval, to feature their Alan, now trading under the name of Big Al Rowbottom (ex booby of this parish), against his supposed tormentors Bobby Jordan and Freddie McKay.

When the news leaked out from the staff room, the pupils immediately tagged it as *The Bruisers v The Booby*.

Meet the bruisers: Bobby Jordan, at 15, was a good playground scrapper with an ear and a nose to prove it. His boxing buddy, Freddie McKay, was a red-headed Scot, who had developed all the right muscles when helping his father on a building site in the school holidays.

The heavily promoted moral of these contests, was, that with care, courage and a boxing instructor, a bullied underdog could emerge with dignity, to take on their aggressors in the Noble Art of Self Defence.

In the meantime, despite repeated requests for a pukka boxing ring, the day of the exhibition dawned with four long wooden children's benches arranged into an improvised square ring.

Since both teachers and parents, particularly the Rowbottoms, had a committed moral agenda, it was decided to hold the event in the evening, so that parents could attend, and to charge a shilling entrance fee to benefit the boxing club.

Having passed through a quiet betting period at school, due to my transfer into a higher stream and being forced to catch up on the previous terms venture into algebra, the arrival of the boxing contests came not only as a pleasant relief, but in the climate, a golden opportunity for making a bit of cash.

After a little meditation, rarely practised at Goldsworth, I came to the conclusion that the simplest and most attractive way to make a book was by offering prices on the double result, i.e. win, lose or draw on the Jordan v Rowbottom contest, doubled with a win, lose or draw on the following McKay v Rowbottom event.

Despite the newfound reputation of Rowbottom, those wanting a bet could not believe he would have the courage and tenacity to match the playground bruisers. Therefore, a 'Bruiser/Bruiser double', as it became known, proved a popular bet at 6-4, while the 4-1 for Rowbottom to win both fights was scorned.

Interestingly, very few punters favoured a mixed result, since according to Tich Talbot: 'Either you believe that "pudding face" can box or not.' Put like that, it was hard to dispute his simple logic.

In the lead up to the Friday night event, my business was surprisingly slow – just a dozen or so tanners and bobs, almost all on a double bruiser victory. Except, that was, for Shirley, who for two terms appeared joined at the hip to Alan; some even said it went further than that. Sentimentally, but with purpose, she found a half-crown for a win double on her ex-boyfriend.

During assembly on the Friday morning, Bonk and Bill Long, the games master and incidentally my new algebra teacher, made some stirring speeches about the need for fair play and there being no room for bullies in the new Elizabethan era. Then, as in a surreal dream, Alan Rowbottom stepped out from behind a curtain, gloved up and in a blue silk dressing gown. At first, there was a stunned silence, until Tich Talbot blurted out, 'Blimey, who does he think he is, Freddie Mills?' The laughter that followed quickly turned into spontaneous applause, which was taken up by Bonk and the staff. Meanwhile, Talbot's intervention was passed on from row to row to the back of the hall, making the episode all the more memorable.

The following lunch break, there was a surge of interest in the fight odds, particularly from those who had received their weekly pocket money. However, in spite of that morning's presentation of 'Big Al', sympathies were now mixed, many pupils believing that whilst Al could possibly beat Jordan, he would never beat Freddie McKay, who was something of a playground hero.

The evening arrived and with an air of expectancy, a crowd of around

50 adults and many more children packed into the school hall.

In an attempt to keep my betting book clear of the teachers, I adopted an innocent posture in a middle row.

After an introduction from Bill Long and an address by the secretary of the boxing club, two small boys from the club gave an exhibition bout, which in reality looked more like two flailing windmills. However, the audience enjoyed the entertainment and were generous in their appreciation, awarding them a thunderous round of applause.

Bill Long then stepped forward to introduce the main event.

'In the red corner in white trunks and singlet, representing the Woking Boxing Club, we have Big Al Rowbottom. And, in the blue corner, with blue shorts and singlet, our own Bobby Jordan – will the Jordan roll tonight?' he added with a grin.

Long was always a very fair teacher, upright and ex-RAF. He had become a role model for me; even so, he knew how to give me a good slippering when I needed it.

After handing over to the referee, he rang the school hand bell to start the fight. In the first minute both boxers stayed close to each other, with much holding and feinting, until, towards the end of the round, Jordan landed a solid dig into Al's ribs to send him down on one knee. Up soon after, his seconds worked on him in the interval, encouraging deep breathes, occasionally brought to a halt by a sharp intake of smelling salts.

The boxers touched gloves for the second and final round. Rowbottom, with instructions from his corner, and showing off his newfound skills, proceeded to dance around out of Jordan's reach, before landing a straight left and an uppercut to send Bobby sprawling. The Jordan was certainly rolling now and, sadly, he failed to beat the count.

Quaintly, tea and biscuits were served in the interval at a tanner a throw, while I discreetly warded off an anxious queue of punters keen to hedge their bets.

Rowbottom, due to his training, was now thought by the shrewdies fit enough to fight another two rounds.

Bill Long once again introduced the boxers: 'In the red corner – Big Al Rowbottom – already an impressive winner tonight. And, over in the blue corner, our own 'Fearless' Freddie McKay – out to prove *Scotland the Brave*!'

Cue Ma Snow, an English teacher, giving a spirited rendering of said tune on the nearby piano – to meet with more applause, some for Freddie, holding his arms aloft as if he had already won, but thoughtfully some for Ma Snow's entertaining performance.

The referee brought the boxers to the centre of the ring.

'You both know the rules, now touch gloves and come out fighting.' They did, hammer and tongs, Freddie hanging on to Al for the latter part of round one.

During the minute interval there was much towel waving and gargling of salt water, before they faced up for the final two minutes.

Rowbottom came out for the second round, dancing as before in an attempt to keep away from Freddie, who in desperation chased after him.

Then, amid all the shouting, a shrill and plaintive female voice threaded through from the second row – it was Shirley, and in a desperate plea to her loved one, she cried out, 'Go on Alan darling, sock him, sock him real hard.'

It took less than a second. Big Al, recognising the shrill voice above the noise and losing his concentration, turned to face her. Wham – Freddie caught him square on the jaw. But Al didn't go down; he just stood there looking dazed. Seconds later the bell went to end the fight. Pupils started chanting 'Fred-die, Fred-die,' as the judges totalled up the points. Bill Long took the microphone and the referee brought the boxers together.

'Ladies and Gentlemen, the official result from our three judges is … (a long pause) … a draw.'

Some boos broke out from disgruntled punters, but Bonk, to give him his due, took over to congratulate both boy boxers on a splendid show, particularly thanking Mr and Mrs Rowbottom for 'a glimpse into the Noble Art of Self Defence.' After which the parents clapped, bringing an end to the proceedings.

On the betting front I had done very well, thanks to Shirley, the real hero of the evening in my books, since no-one had backed a Big Al win-draw double, generously offered I thought, at 20-1.

On totting up the tanner and bob bets I had made an amazing two quid profit, the equivalent of nearly seven weeks' paper round money. However, I wasn't in the clear yet.

As the parents and teachers filtered out of the hall, volunteers from the boxing club stood by the doors with collecting tins.

Just behind me, I could hear Billy Barker, a regular punter with me, getting nearer. Then, sidling up to me, he said in a loud voice: 'Come on Churchy, cough up, you must have made a packet on that last fight?'

I could also see Bonk just a few yards behind him, talking to the Rowbottoms.

I could be in serious trouble here, I feared.

Thinking quickly, I hissed to Barker, 'OK, ok, keep it down. I'll put a ten bob note in, OK.'

Barker grinned – he knew how it hurt me, but we still left the best of friends.

On Monday morning, I was surprisingly accosted by Bonk in the playground.

'Church, I glimpsed your contribution to the boxing club on Friday night, admirable, admirable. You should take it up yourself you know, better than burying your head in the racing papers.'

# CHAPTER FIVE

## A Black Horse, a Very Black Horse

The story that follows has been put together from fragments told to me throughout my childhood.

My nan – Alicia Margaret – being careful not to give me all of the sad and lurid details at too early an age, allowed her sister (my great aunt Kate), especially near Derby Day, to tell me the more joyful aspects of their adventure.

However, when I was old enough to fit the pieces together, other members of the family kindly filled in the gaps, so authenticating this strange and romantic tale.

After the end of the First World War, the Derby, having been run at Newmarket for the duration, returned to Epsom in 1919. It seemed that everyone wanted to be there, as if taking up the reins again of a British way of life. Their Majesties King George V and Queen Mary, together with other members of the Royal family were in attendance and, somewhere out on the Downs, so were great aunt Kate and my nan, Alicia Margaret. Neither had been to the Derby before but both in their way had kept an interest in the Turf and, on big race days, entrusted their two-shilling each-way bets by way of the milkman.

Kate, from her photo at the time, looked handsome, slim, and more than a little melancholy after her boyfriend, Charlie, a captain in the Royal Artillery, had been reported missing after the battle of Cambrai in north-east France. They had been very much in love and now with no news of him for nearly two years, she had all but given up hope.

However, today, Derby Day, Kate and nan were out to enjoy themselves. They watched sword swallowers, escapologists, and even took their chance on the coconut shy, until eventually, they were drawn to the row of small tents housing the fortune-tellers. And although there must have been three 'Original Gypsy Rose Lea's' and even a sister to the original, Kate was attracted to one bearing a name like her own: '*Princess Katrina – Star of the East – Fortunes told for sixpence.*'

The inside of the tent was draped in black net curtains with a few gold stars stuck on for effect. A very wizened Princess Katrina, wearing a black and gold headdress, sat at a small round table, in the middle of which, was a crystal ball under a large gold handkerchief.

Katrina bade them sit down and proceeded to ask them if they had come for a special reason. Kate had not really thought about it beforehand, although a year ago, she had gone to a séance to enquire of her beloved Charlie.

Suddenly, she blurted out, 'I've a boyfriend, still reported missing from the war; Charlie his name is. He's a captain in the Royal Artillery.' It sounded hopeless, she began to cry and nan held her hand.

Katrina stared into the ball, occasionally murmuring, 'I do see a Charlie, but he's not in uniform,' then looking up and smiling, she said: 'Today is a good day for you. Is it your birthday or an anniversary of something?'

'No, I don't think so,' replied Kate.

'It's just that the 4th of June keeps appearing – that's today – today is your lucky day ladies,' she smiled again.

Kate and Alicia remained silent.

Katrina returned her concentration to the glass ball.

'I can see coming through the haze, a black horse, a very black horse, and crowds of people. Drat, it's faded away. What a pity.' Then before

Kate or Alicia could say anything, Katrina said, 'Time's up, I'm afraid, that will be sixpence each.' Alicia and Kate stumbled out of the tent into the hurly-burly of Epsom Downs.

'What did you make of that?' Alicia asked Kate.

'Well I'm a little confused. Charlie would have been in uniform, and what was all that about a black horse?'

'And the date?' added nan.

'Oh well,' sighed Kate, 'Let's look at the racing, remember, today's our lucky day!'

'You don't suppose there's a black horse in the Derby do you?' enquired Alicia.

There was – Grand Parade.

'But not much chance,' Kate said, looking in her *Daily Sketch*. 'It's 33-1 in here. Still, I suppose we should have a bit on each-way.'

It was difficult to see anything, the crowds were enormous and Alicia, being only four feet nine inches was at a distinct disadvantage. But, having put their bets on, totalling, an extravagant ten shillings each way on Grand Parade, Alicia courageously asked Ted Baxter – the bookie – if she could stand on his chair to watch the race. As the runners approached and the noise reached a crescendo, Ted lifted her on to the chair, while his clerk, Fred, attentively helped Kate onto his stool.

Joy of joys, they saw Grand Parade's colours – black with a red, white and blue sash – come thundering past to beat the light blue, pink sash and cap of Lord Astor's Buchan by half a length.

'Did we win, did we win?' Kate asked Ted excitedly.

'Come on you two, I'll help you down. Suppose you want me to give you your money? Fred, ticket number 481.'

Fred ran his finger down the ledger, 'Twenty-one pound, twelve and six,' he groaned – the equivalent of a working-man's monthly

*Grand Parade beats Buchan in the 'Peace Derby' of 1919*

take-home pay. The girls agreed – 'Good old Katrina.'

A year on, they still spoke of the fortune teller and their big win, but for Kate and Alicia things had changed – for the worse.

Kate accepted that she would probably never see Captain Charles again, while Alicia was now faced with the true extent of my grandfather's philandering.

But for all that, on Derby Day, although unable to attend, Kate and Alicia got together for a cup of tea and a chin-wag, having first put a few bob on Steve Donoghue. As it happened, Steve had a couple of winners, but had no luck in the Derby, when in the closing stages of the race his Abbots Trace crossed its legs and fell.

On the Friday, Oaks day, Alicia's husband, Ernest, had left his *Sporting Life* on the table before going to work. Alicia, taking a break from her household chores, picked up the paper. Looking at the headlines, she noticed the date – 4 June 1920.

'Fourth of June, fourth of June,' she repeated to herself. Suddenly it came back to her – the gypsy princess – that was the date, in the crystal ball.

Soon after, while scanning the Oaks runners, she spotted the name Charlebelle.

'Fancy that,' she mused. 'Kate was once Charlie's belle; not anymore though. Perhaps I ought to have a couple of bob on it anyway.'

Then, reading a summary of the race, a shiver went down Alicia's spine: 'the black filly Charlebelle, a beaten favourite last time out, looks certain to improve.'

'Black filly – June 4'. That was enough.

Getting her coat, she hurried round to Kate's place, to catch her returning from her morning job at the Co-op.

'Kate let's go in, I've got something to show you.'

Alicia spread out the paper, while Kate put the kettle on.

'Well that is a coincidence,' said Kate. 'Another black horse and on the fourth of June. We've got to back it.'

Kate went to the sideboard. 'Look, I've got 25 bob here that I've been saving for the Tally man,' she said recklessly.

'And I'll put the same,' said Alicia, having recently pawned a pair of silver candlesticks that were given to her as a wedding present.

'The old bugger won't know they've gone – he's never at home!'

So round to the drop-off point in West Street and 25 bob each-way on Charlebelle.

'We must be mad,' said Alicia. Kate agreed.

Later that afternoon, the two of them sat and waited. No television of course, no commentary on the radio and the stop press result for the Oaks would not be in the evening papers until later.

'I know,' said Kate, 'let's get over to Enticknap's in Church Path.' Enticknap was Woking's only legal credit bookmaker – their bet had gone through a runner and was strictly cash, but the office had a tickertape machine!

So round they went – bold as brass – up the stairs and knocked at the door.

'Three minutes before the "off",' Kate said, nervously looking at her watch and then across to Alicia.

'Yes Ladies,' a gaunt looking face appeared at the small sliding hatch door, as if in a speakeasy.

Kate, finding courage from somewhere, said: 'Would you mind if we watched the result of the Oaks coming through on your tickertape?'

'Blimey, what's the world coming to; we'll have children asking to come in next!'

He unlocked the door.

'Do you know anyone in here?' he asked. They looked around the

*Alicia and Ernest
– trouble brewing*

smoke-filled room at about a dozen men and one woman. Alicia's face was filled with horror.

'That's my husband over there, with that woman.'

The gaunt betting clerk called across, 'Alright if your wife comes in Ernie?'

But Alicia didn't wait for the answer and neither did Kate.

Then, as Kate set foot down the stairs, a voice came from behind.

'Remember me? It's Fred. I put you up on my stool – at the Derby last year.'

Kate remembered, but with Alicia rushing out of the front door, she had only time to give him a warm smile and say goodbye.

However, the next day they read: 'Charlebelle beats Cinna a neck in the Oaks – black filly lands a coup for the Druid's Lodge Confederacy.'

Thereafter, spurred on by the good references of Alicia and Kate, many well-wishers from the betting fraternity tried to trace Princess Katrina. Alas, none was successful.

Nevertheless, there was a twist in this tale for Kate, for since Fred had started clerking for Enticknap, he had begun to see more and more of her.

That winter, Kate went with Fred to Kempton. He had been offered a couple of days clerking for Harry Nelson, a local bookie. And when asked to show a reference, and his driving licence, if he had one, Fred produced the necessary. Harry looked them over.

'Why is the reference for Fred Stubbs and the driving licence for Charles Frederick Stubbs?' Nelson enquired.

'Oh, the first bookie I clerked for was called Charlie, and it got a bit confusing on the phone. So I used Fred, and when I moved on, everyone still called me Fred.'

Standing nearby, Kate's expression lit up. Suddenly, Fred became her new Charlie and she his Charlebelle!

*For the record Grand Parade was the last black horse to win the Derby, and Charlebelle the last black filly to win the Oaks.*

*Interestingly, of the 2007 foal crop, Weatherbys inform me that only 0.3% of GB foals and 0.1% of Irish foals were registered as black.*

*Years later – Alicia and Kate*
*remembering*

# CHAPTER SIX

## *A Red Dog of a Different Colour*

'Have you seen the new greyhound paper out this week Charlie – *The Greyhound Express*? All dogs it is, except for the back page, and that's horses. You get this, you don't need another paper!'

Roy and Charlie boarded the fast train at Woking – first stop London Waterloo. They were bound for White City; it was Greyhound Derby Final night, the year, 1932.

Had you been on their Central Line underground train you might have guessed anyway. Hundreds of young men, and a few women, strap hanging, swaying, and more than a few reading the new paper. White City had become the Mecca of this fascinating sport and tonight an unbelievable crowd of 80,000 people would push through the turnstiles to see a race that would go down in history.

Even so, the reason for Charlie and Roy's attendance, and they insisted on this when they told me some 20 years later, was to back a white dog in a red jacket earlier on the card – or as Charlie put it, a red dog of a different colour.

The greyhound was known to them as Jack, or sometimes Jack o'Lantern when appearing on the London flapping tracks. But more of that later.

Spilling out from the tube station, they were swept along the road towards the track, like the course of a river.

Charlie, a bricklayer and one of the nine Church brothers, had been a fan of the dogs for almost three years, taking in the exploits of the legendary Mick the Miller. Meantime, Charlie's pal Roy was a bookie's runner, who would call every day at the Churches home in West Street, to pick up and pay out bets; number 45 being one of the 'safer houses', during the years in which illegal betting flourished.

Forging their way down the street, they were constantly approached by men selling out of suitcases – watches, clothing, tin foods, quite apart from the tipsters and programme sellers. Nearing the stadium, one van, driven off the road near one of the entrances, was selling a pile of white boxes. Charlie, being inquisitive, pushed in to see.

'They're shoes Roy. All leather, hand-made shoes, Oxford style. Fallen off the back of a lorry in the West End, only this morning!'

Roy came to look. They were selling fast, that's for sure. And Roy said he could do with a posh pair of shoes for when he went racing. They weren't cheap, unless they were the real thing that was. Like almost everything Roy did, it was a gamble and he took it.

'Have you got two pairs of size nines there?' he asked the spiv, remembering generously that Charlie took the same size. A well-worn camel-coat dived into the back of the van.

'Two nines coming up Gov. Two quid each, OK.'

'Two quid.' recoiled Roy, 'that's a bit steep.'

'A bit steep,' the spiv objected. 'You won't see the likes of these for two quid anywhere else – they're a steal!'

And so they were.

Roy and Charlie joined the long queues to the turnstiles with shoeboxes underarm. People had been arriving at the track from the middle of the afternoon, many with their own food and drink, enough to last them the evening. For such were the crowds inside the stadium, that in order to get a meat pie and a cup of tea, you would run the risk of missing a race and not getting a bet on.

Eventually, after waiting more than half an hour, Roy and Charlie got inside the stadium.

At this point, I think it best that Charlie tells you the story as he told me.

'Inside White City, it looked more like a Cup Final than a dog meeting; the size of the crowd was staggering. Quite apart from all the pushing and shoving, there were long lines to get to the Tote windows, and large clusters of punters hovering in front of the 200 or so bookmakers spread round the track. There was also a military band on the go: 'Pack Up Your Troubles, Tipperary', and that sort of thing, although most of us were too busy, either studying the form, or trying to get a bet on, to take much notice.

'You see, Roy had been given this strong tip from his governor that 'Jack o'Lantern', shall we call him, would be on a going night and, we should get on, bundles if we could.

'We decided that a tenner each was the best we could muster (a monster bet for a working man at the time), and when the time came, we positioned ourselves within striking distance of the boards of O'Hara and Billy Broadbent.

'During the parade we kept a careful eye on Jack, his powerful white frame contrasting with the red jacket under the glare of the lights. Then, just before they went in the traps we made our move. O'Hara laid me, £55 to £10, while seconds later, Broadbent laid Roy £50 to £10.

'We were on and the hare was running.'

Uncle Charlie recalled the race as if it was happening in front of him.

'The favourite was in the five box and he got a flyer; two lengths up before the bend. Jack, as we knew, was often slowly away and so he was tonight. But it looked as if he had a bit of trackcraft, and going into the second bend he kept on the rails, moving up to third down the back straight. Around the final bend, he still had a length to make up on the favourite, but he kept gaining, and hugging the rails he went by to win by a neck.

'I'm sweating now just thinking about it,' Charlie said, as he reached in his top pocket for a handkerchief.

'Tell Michael about the shoeboxes,' interrupted Roy, enjoying the telling as much as Charlie.

'Oh yeah, the shoeboxes, but first came the track announcement over the Tannoy. Apparently, gangs of pickpockets were at work in the crowds, lifting wallets and watches. Then Roy came up with this bright idea,' Roy beamed, as Charlie continued.

'We would go to the lavatory and empty our wallets into the toes of the shoes in the boxes; all except for two fivers – one to celebrate with and the other for emergencies. We reckoned if we were going to get turned over, or hit on the head going home, the last thing they would rob us for was a pair of shoes.

'Anyway, after about seven races our feet were beginning to give us gyp, so back to the lavs, to switch the cash into our old shoes and try on the new ones.

'Now I know what your thinking Michael, but you'd be wrong, they fitted like gloves, real toff's shoes they were.'

'And that was another shrewd move,' interrupted Roy, 'You see, no-one would be interested in robbing us for two scruffy pair of shoes.'

However, by now, even to this 16-year-old, Roy and Charlie were becoming a tad obsessive.

'Tell us about the Derby,' I pressed, pouring both our visitors another bottle of Bass each. Charlie took a drink, wiped his lips and continued.

'Oh yes, I must tell you that before the dogs came out for the final, they paraded four previous Derby winners, including the great Mick the Miller – he got a fantastic cheer from the crowd. It made you feel as if you were part of history. But back to the race. From the bookies boards it looked like a two-dog race: 8-13 Future Cutlet (trap 5); 5-2 Wild Woolley (trap 6), and 10-1 bar. Both dogs had won their semis, but in a first round heat Future Cutlet had beaten Woolley fair and square, to set a new track record.

'However, despite all the excitement, neither Roy nor I, wanted to have a bet – you see we had already made our money for the night and there didn't seem any sense in opening the shoeboxes again.'

Mum and dad started to laugh, visualising Charlie and Roy opening their shoeboxes in front of the bookies!

Charlie pressed on, hardly breaking stride.

'With all the noise going on – I guess you could call it the Derby roar – neither of the favourites broke well. However, Future Cutlet soon took off and crossing to the rails forced Woolley wide. Along the back straight, it was as we expected, a two-dog race, with Woolley chasing hard. Neck and neck into the third bend, Woolley had regained the rails and, when the improving Cutlet ran wide at the last – some said the driver had slowed the hare – Woolley pressed his advantage to win by a diminishing neck. The distance between second and third was ten lengths and the time, 29.72, was a record for the 525-yard final.'

Charlie's impressive account brought dad to say that he should challenge Leslie Welch (the memory man) on the radio.

Suddenly, Charlie looked a bit embarrassed. 'Have you got another Bass there Dorothy,' he said to mum, offering his glass.

Roy, taking advantage of the lull, then said, 'Shall I tell 'em about the presentation of the trophy, Charlie?'

'Oh yeah, go on, Dorothy will like that.'

'Well, Charlie and I worked our way along to the area where we could see the ceremony. Lady Chatham, a good-looking woman, presented an impressive looking trophy to the owner, Sam Johnson of Manchester. Apparently, he had only paid 25 guineas for the dog. Imagine that, Charlie and I had won four times that amount on Jack. Also, I must tell you, that Wild Woolley, a dark brindle, by the way, had the special 1932 Derby winner's jacket put on, before they paraded him around the track.'

With Charlie having run out of steam, it was Roy who revealed their nightmare journey home.

'After a couple more drinks in the stadium, we joined the 500-yard queue at White City underground station and then, onto the overcrowded platforms at Tottenham Court Road. Eventually, to cap it all, when we got to Waterloo, a guard told us that there was a Sunday service in operation.'

At this point, Charlie, having downed the Bass, continued the story.

'I remember saying something like, "Oh bugger this, let's have another drink and then get a cab – all the way to Woking".

'However, I don't remember much of the journey, apart from us singing, with the cabbie joining in, friendly like. It had been a great night, so we tipped him handsomely and waved goodbye.'

'A minute later, as we staggered through the front door, it hit us simultaneously – **the shoeboxes, the bloody shoeboxes!!**

'All that money and we'd left it in the bloody cab.

'We were desolate – neither of us slept that night. We had no receipt for the fare, we hadn't taken the cab number, I mean, why would we?'

Charlie continued, 'On Monday, the pain grew worse when our pals asked us if we'd had a good time at White City. And Roy's boss, who

*Wild Woolley – winner of the 1932 Greyhound Derby*

had given him the tip, was gobsmacked at our stupidity. Ain't that right Roy?'

Roy cut in for the finale.

'But miraculously, there was a happy ending. The following Friday, Jane (dad's mum), opened the front door to a grinning taxi driver who handed her our two white shoeboxes. The cabbie told Jane, 'I dropped a fare here last Saturday night; two blokes who couldn't stop singing; I reckon anyone who carries such scruffy old shoes around with them must really need them. So here they are. And thank them again for the fat tip.'

'That evening,' Roy concluded, 'Mrs Stebbings, our neighbour, said she heard Charlie shouting and laughing from as far as four doors away. 'It's amazing, just amazing,' he kept shouting – 'Taxi driver, I love you.'

Looking back, Charlie's story went some way to explaining a phenomenon that had always puzzled me.

Why Charlie, although a heavy bettor, but in every other way a reluctant spender, was such a generous tipper.

*Footnote: Trained by Jimmy Rimmer, Wild Woolley went on to run in the Greyhound Derby a further three times. In the 1933 final, he finished third to his old rival Future Cutlet and in 1934, he finished third again, this time to Davesland. Finally, in 1935, now five years old, he was eliminated in the first round heats and subsequently retired to stud.*

# CHAPTER SEVEN

## *An Irish Sweeps Ticket*

The postman wasn't usually late, but he was this morning. And so George, who usually opened his letters on the train to Hatch End, read his *Daily Mirror* instead.

George, my future father-in-law, managed the Rothmans cigarette factory, just across the road from the railway station. He had been at Rothmans for seven years, having previously served as a batman in the Great War, before becoming the senior porter at the Thackeray Hotel (opposite the British Museum), where he first met his wife, Frances.

Frances, then a teenager, had travelled down from Newcastle with her sisters, to seek out a living in London. Applying for the position of chambermaid, her long eyelashes and good looks had attracted George from the moment he showed her into the manager's office. And now, many years later, he and Frances, 16 years his junior, lived comfortably in Hyde Road, Harrow, with their two children – Patricia (my wife to be), and her younger brother Gerald.

When George returned home that night there were two letters waiting for him. One from the Inland Revenue, which he put aside to read later, while the other looked more interesting, as it had an Irish stamp on it.

'What was your post dad?' Fran called out to George.

George went quiet; time for a small celebration he thought and, going to the sideboard, poured himself the last of the Christmas scotch.

'I've drawn a horse in the Irish Sweepstakes – Firemaster.'

'Oh, is that good; has it got a chance?' said Fran, hovering at his side.

'Not much of one. But it's worth a good bit of money and if I can sell half the ticket, I can keep the proceeds, whatever the result.'

'How can you sell half a ticket?' Fran said, puzzled.

'Well, a man I worked with a few years ago, he drew a horse in the Irish Sweeps and soon after, he was approached by some syndicate, bookmakers I think. They bought half his ticket for over a thousand pounds – he bought a brand new Bentley. Funny really, because of the shortage, he couldn't get the petrol to drive it!'

The next morning, George, never one to procrastinate, made the call.

'Charlie, you remember when you sold half your Irish Sweepstake ticket? Yes, I'm fine, and Fran, yes and the kids too.'

George, sensing this was not going to be a quick call, put a further shilling in the box and continued.

'Anyway, why I'm ringing is I've drawn a horse in the Derby. No great shakes I think – it's Firemaster – Lord Rosebery's – a 50-1 shot. But how do I go about selling half the ticket?'

George scribbled the details on the back of an envelope and the next day, diligently and hopefully, joined the queue in a West End hotel where those lucky to draw a horse looked to do a bit of business.

It seemed he had the choice of selling a half or the whole of his ten-shilling ticket to a bookmakers' syndicate for cash, the amount depending on the chance of the horse.

The payments were being calculated at a rate slightly worse than the

current odds, to allow the bookies a profit for their troubles, or if you like, for their opportunity.

The history behind all this started in the 1930s, when the Irish Hospitals' Sweepstake was established as a way of funding the Irish Free State's hospitals. The draw, a showbiz national event, took place at Ballsbridge, near Dublin, where pretty, uniformed nurses drew the winning tickets out of an enormous barrel; these were matched to the declared runners and the lucky punters were informed by post.

Ticket sales ran into millions, so the total prize-money was divided to form many sweeps, roughly one for each £50,000 in the kitty. George had no false hopes – Firemaster was a long shot, a likely also-ran – but after making some enquiries he hoped to sell half his ticket, as a form of insurance, for about £500 – equal to half his annual salary.

The queue ahead moved slowly, some punters trying to negotiate a better payment. In fact, the man two places ahead of George, dressed in overalls, had drawn the second favourite – Blue Train, unbeaten and owned by the King. He had told George that by selling the whole ticket he hoped to plan his retirement – a cottage in Devon and a new motor.

When the overalls got to the front table, there looked to be a serious discussion going on; George thought he overheard £7,000 mentioned.

Suddenly, their dealings were interrupted by a youth clutching a line of tickertape. Then all hell broke loose.

It seemed Blue Train had been withdrawn, lame, and so within that minute the ticket had become worthless. The man in overalls was distraught, knowing that if he had taken the bookies' first offer he would have been rich.

George's heart went out to the man. What a sad story he would take with him. Nevertheless, having followed the bookies' methods of business, he was determined to learn from it.

As it turned out, the scratching of Blue Train did George a small favour, his horse now having a slightly better chance. In consequence, he pocketed £550, with the possibility of a lot more if his horse finished in the first three.

Incidentally, whilst George was up at the table he queried why the date of the race, shown on his sweepstake ticket as 4th June, had been advanced from the traditional Wednesday to Saturday, the 7th.

'That's your Labour Government for you,' a portly bookies' clerk sardonically informed him.

'They don't want the south of England missing work to go racing, do they? Oh no; but funny ain't it, all those aunties and uncles' funerals will now have to be put on hold until next year,' he said, quizzically, through a puff of cigar smoke.

*Frances and George Parish*

On the way home, George decided, as the race was to be run on Saturday, he would go to Epsom to witness what would be for many a life-changing experience.

'What would you like for your lunch George, spam, or cheese and pickle sandwiches?' Fran called across from the kitchen to the dining room, where George was polishing off a large bowl of porridge whilst picking out his horses from the *Daily Mirror*.

'Have you phoned Mr Busby at the factory?' Fran enquired; her hair still in curlers, with a pinafore over her nightdress.

'No, would you do it for me mum,' he replied. 'Tell him, my shrapnel's playing up again and I can't move my shoulder, can't get out of bed, he'll understand.' George got up to go.

'Well good luck dear. I'll listen to the race on the wireless. Oh, and would you put me two bob each-way on Grand Weather, it's such a nice day!'

She saw him off from the front step. George turned and waved. Secretly, he was more excited than he liked to admit. In his quiet way he was quite the opportunist and always nurtured the assumption that he deserved to be, and one day would be, a very rich man. This could be that day!

George turned the corner of the road, trilby, belted raincoat and carrier bag, merging with the crowds going to work.

It was such a nice day, that he came out of Epsom station with his raincoat over his arm and his trilby pushed well down into his carrier bag. There was a long queue for taxis and although he contemplated walking the mile or so up the hill, he walked just far enough into the town to catch a bus.

Strangely, going up to the top deck he got a twinge of pain in his left shoulder – 'Serves me right,' he thought.

George paid his entrance to the Grandstand and was looking for a place to leave his coat and hat, when, heading straight towards him was Mr Busby, the Rothmans factory operations director.

'Hello George, having a day's holiday, grand weather isn't it? Is your wife here?'

George thought quickly. 'Err no; it's her rheumatism you know – in her left shoulder.' He threw that in with some vain hope of causing confusion.

However, by now, he was beginning to realise that Busby had not been to the factory before going to Epsom.

'If only I hadn't asked Fran to phone,' he thought, 'I could have easily sneaked in a holiday request on Busby's desk first thing in the morning.'

'You look as if you could do with a drink, George. I've got a box on the top floor, it's a bit basic, bomb damage and all that you know, but come and join us, it's a great view from up there.'

So George and Mr Busby climbed what seemed like a hundred stairs to the top. If he hadn't needed a drink before, he needed one now – 'Scotch and soda please Mr Busby.'

George was introduced to some of Busby's celebrity friends as a good and faithful worker – 'First there in the morning and last to leave at night; First World War veteran; salt of the earth.' The more Busby heaped on the praise the worse George felt. For he knew that when Busby eventually got Fran's message, he was going to need Firemaster to win the Derby.

Mr Busby's box had a maid. She put the food out, poured the drinks and directed the guests to a makeshift Tote outlet along the corridor. George went along and put Fran's bet on Grand Weather.

When it was time for the Derby, everyone squeezed out on to the balcony. The guests seemed totally committed to Tudor Minstrel, referred to in the press as 'The Horse of the Century'. He had won the 2,000 Guineas by eight lengths and although at the prohibitive odds of 4-7, everyone wanted Gordon Richards to win his first Derby.

George followed the others out to the balcony, but as the shortest person in the room he could see nothing.

For the racegoer in 1947, there were neither racecourse commentaries, nor big screens. So George, heart pounding at the shout, 'They're Off', went in search of a radio.

Five minutes later, George returned to the box, still not knowing the result, but going out onto the balcony as others were coming in, he saw the numbers go up in the frame.

Checking his racecard, he learnt that 18, Pearl Diver, a French outsider, had won, followed home by Migoli and Sayajirao. Further enquiries informed him that Tudor Minstrel and Gordon Richards were only fourth, but no-one remembered where Firemaster or Grand Weather had finished.

George was seldom despondent, but he was now.

'Any luck George?' Busby boomed across the confined space of his box.

'Afraid not,' said George stoically.

'Oh by the way, I rang the factory. My secretary said your wife had left a message,' George held his breath as his P45 passed before his eyes.

'But it was a bad line and she couldn't understand her Geordie accent. Anyway, you didn't tell me you'd drawn a horse in the Irish Sweepstake – you're a cool one George, I like your style. Come and see me Monday, we must have a chat about some ideas I have for you.'

That night, George's thoughts were of a philosophical nature. He'd had a lucky break and maybe, just maybe, different opportunities lay ahead.

# CHAPTER EIGHT

## *The Legacy*

On most Saturday mornings and indeed on this occasion, Uncle Arthur, a shell-shocked First World War veteran, made his weekly trip to the public baths, before visiting my mum and dad.

Arthur, an ex-drill sergeant, had seen repeated action in France and Belgium with dire consequences, none of which endeared him to his fellow man. His severe stammer and head shaking were in addition to his frequent bowel movements – a combination that produced a nervous acceptance amongst his brothers.

But on this day he had some exciting news – a letter from a solicitor in Lyon, informing him that he had been gifted a small stud farm in the will of the widow Adele Leclerc.

Arthur had been involved in a passionate affair with Adele Leclerc during the war, and apparently, she had continued to burn a flame for him, just kept alive by his Christmas and birthday cards and occasional letters of vague promises.

A few years after the Second World War, Adele moved to Lyon to take over the running of her late father's small stud farm, until she later died a widow without heir.

My mum's advice to Uncle Arthur was that he should use our family solicitors, conveniently situated near Woking railway station and within walking distance of his home. This he boldly did and enlisted the assistance of his elder brother Ernie, who by the way, was more fluent than Arthur in both French and English. Together they planned a trip to Lyon, via Dover and Calais, to seek out his legacy.

Brother Albert, of previous racing tales, not wishing to miss out on the excitement, held a 'bon voyage' party for his brothers, suggesting that Arthur could very well become the next Marcel Boussac – a name fresh in our minds having, this year, 1950, bred the winners of both the Derby and Oaks.

The journey proved more difficult than was first thought, with many unscheduled stops because of Arthur's condition. However, two days after leaving Woking they arrived at Lyon railway station and, after a further half-hour taxi drive, they turned into a lane signposted Leclerc Stud Farm.

Arthur and Ernie nervously waited outside the gatehouse with their two small cardboard suitcases. Ernie rang the bell and hoped they had received his telegram.

After a few minutes an elderly man came towards them, sleeves rolled up and trousers tied at the bottom with rough string. He announced himself as Henri the stud manager and as having only a basic understanding of English, but yes, he had received their telegram.

Henri took them down a muddy path, past two dilapidated barns, before taking them through the back door of his house. Greeted by his wife Camille the brothers were made welcome.

Arthur and Ernie could tell by now that all was not as they had hoped for, but the story of the stud's decline was told to them in a straight and simple manner. It had been necessary for Adele to remortgage the stud to pay off her father's debts and to pay Henri's wages and

*Church Brothers – L to R – Stan, Arthur, Charlie,
with George and Ernie seated*

general running expenses. They stood two stallions, but neither were well patronised and both horses were now into their late twenties. The dreams of Arthur and Ernie receded further by the minute and, despite the very hospitable supper and good red wine provided by Camille, the brothers went to bed with more questions than answers.

The following day, Henri drove them into Lyon to meet the solicitors and for Arthur to learn the extent of his inheritance. Henri's son, Henri junior, had also arranged to be there, mainly as support for his father, but also should a business opportunity arise.

The solicitor, with use of an interpreter, put the details before them.

In a nutshell, the assets had been surpassed by the continuing debts and mortgage. If Arthur wanted to save the stud farm from bankruptcy he would have to find a minimum of 14,000 francs, the equivalent of £2,800 at the time. Sadly, Arthur's total finances consisted only of a small army pension and his 'old age pension' – just enough to live on.

After their meeting, Henri junior took the brothers, his father and the solicitor all to lunch, where informally, they put together a rescue plan to relieve Arthur from his impending debt, while keeping Henri and Camille on at the stud. In short, Henri junior would buy them out for a nominal sum.

Ernie, a cautious man, felt things were moving so fast, that he feared that Arthur may be being taken for a ride. But at least Arthur had the good sense not to sign anything, until as he said, 'P-P-Putting the f-facts before the W-W-Woking solicitors.'

However, the more they went into the figures and discussed the alternative outcomes, the more Henri junior's offer looked the best way forward for Arthur, until, finally, the brothers had to agree, at least in principle, to the buy-out proposal.

It was as if a great weight had been taken off Arthur's shoulders. That evening he laughed, chatted and stammered his way through supper and when Camille brought out the old photographs of Adele, and in particular, one she had found of Adele and Arthur together, he could hold back the tears no longer.

The next morning, Arthur and Ernie started to consider their return trip, and although Camille suggested that they may like to stay a little longer, Henri junior came down to breakfast with his own plan – one that would show the brothers the sunnier side of France.

He had recently acquired a run-down property in the Old Town area of Menton, midway between Monaco and Italy. He needed to assess the cost of doing it up, before selling it on. So, if the brothers didn't mind roughing it a bit, the three of them could travel down to the Riviera in his van and drive along the coast to Menton. It was a long journey, but they would see the Mediterranean and have a tale to tell when they got back to Woking.

It seems strange now, but in 1950, apart from the wealthy, very few Englishmen had visited France, other than to fight in the two World Wars.

Their journey, pre-motorways, proved testing – winding roads and hairpin bends – until finally coming out at Grasse, where they stayed for the night. Thereafter, they made the short trip to Cannes, then Nice, Monte Carlo and Menton.

This was to have a great effect on the brothers. For them, it was like another world – the sunshine, temperatures in the 80s, exotic fruits, and strangely, food cooked in olive oil. However, they both agreed they could easily get used to this life.

Henri junior found the Old Town. His place was a top floor apartment along a very narrow street paved with flagstones – opposite flats could have shared the same washing line and it looked as if some did.

Henri had only been there once before, but enough to warn the brothers of the 40 steep stone steps to his flat. There was no light at the top of the staircase, so Arthur had to strike a couple of matches, while Henri found his keys. However, there were light bulbs working inside, enough for Arthur to find his way to the lavatory and, joy of joys, the flushing cistern worked.

Henri quickly went around checking the water flow from the taps and finding the fuse box. The outside shutters, however, were jammed shut and although the three men were able to open a few a little way, some were so rotten that they came off their hinges. Even to the brothers, who had lived their lives in an old, two-bedroomed terraced house, there looked to be a lot of work needed to get this apartment fit to sell or rent.

However, they rose to the occasion, had a makeshift meal and due to the warm night slept on top of their beds.

The next morning, the brothers amused themselves exploring the Old Town, while Henri went in search of a carpenter and an electrician.

Henri was very good with the brothers, apologising for the mess and the inconvenience, while mindful of the need to keep them happy with an eye to his future.

That evening, he took them out for a meal at a restaurant within walking distance. It was there that Henri decided that they all needed a bit of excitement and suggested that the following evening they go along the Riviera to the casino at Monte Carlo.

At this time, there was a strict dress code at the Casino, gently enforced by what looked like two all-in wrestlers standing either side of the main entrance. Therefore, it was jackets and ties for men and, an admission fee to boot. Henri took care of it all, spotting a war veteran with his dog, standing some way off, selling ties from a huge tray slung around his neck. A few minutes later, Henri, Arthur and Ernie were ushered through the great swing doors of the casino, wearing matching hand-painted ties of tumbling dice.

To Arthur and Ernie the casino looked like Buckingham Palace – such splendour, such opulence. Henri drew their attention to the wonderfully ornate ceilings. Nevertheless, as always, it was the lavatories that impressed Arthur.

Coming up trumps again, Henri had sportingly bought a stack of chips for each of them and eventually, the three hopefuls got to the roulette tables. The crowds were particularly deep that night and they would have to wait a while just to get into the second row surrounding the table. Mulling it over, Henri and Ernie decided to buy a beer instead and left Arthur to it.

Arthur hadn't played before, but he watched the other players intently. After a few minutes he had worked out a plan to back numbers four and five – not that they were due an appearance, or, that he had been watching the moment the croupier dropped in the ball. No, it was because he lived at 45 West Street, so that had to be lucky for him, or did it?

Arthur's stack of chips was slowly disappearing; he had just five one-franc chips left, worth about a pound. He could have eked them out by playing one number at a time, but he continued his system of putting one chip on number four and one on five. Arthur waited, and watched the ball whizz round the wheel until – 'Numero Quatre, Noir, Manque'.

'That's m-m-me', stammered Arthur. Sadly, the excitement affected his bowels and, trustingly, he asked the elderly lady next to him to 'watch over my winnings, I'll be back very soon.' And to give him his due he was.

Arthur returned to the table amidst a burst of applause.

'Oh there you are,' the lady said, 'You have been lucky. I left the chips on number four, just like you wanted, but the croupier had to change them to the stripy ones, anyway you won again. You are a lucky man! Look, you see, I have kept them here for you.'

Arthur was dumbstruck, but whilst he was puzzling what to do next, he caught sight of Ernie and waved him over. Henri too joined they fray. Drinks were ordered and chips cashed. Ernie told them he too had been winning, but only ten francs from a slot machine, while Henri junior had lost his stack on the blackjack tables.

All in all Arthur had won over £250, this at a time when a good wage in Britain was £10 a week.

A few days later, they considered going back to Monte to play again, but Arthur, still having difficulty in believing his good fortune, feared to return. As he explained, 'What 'appens if they recognise m-me and say it was all a m-m-mistake and I have to g-give it all b-b-back?'

And, since no amount of reasoning would change Arthur's mind, it was agreed it would be best if they caught the return train home, particularly as Henri's tradesmen were working full-time in the apartment and the continual banging and clanking was beginning to upset Arthur's shell-shocked nerves.

Back in Woking, Arthur and Ernie were welcomed home as if they had been to the moon.

The British Legion, as part of a Friday night entertainment, had asked them to give a brief account of their travels. However, whilst Ernie's rather shy account was well received, the Master of Ceremonies had failed to remember Arthur's impediment, and so his brief account became considerably longer. Nevertheless, he got the biggest cheer of the night when he called for the barman to, 'F-f-fill everyone's glass for a d-d-drink on m-me.'

Thereafter, every Saturday morning for nearly a year, Arthur would call on us to say he had received no news from the Woking solicitors.

Then, one foggy morning in November, Arthur's beaming face appeared at the kitchen window. At last, he had received a letter finalising the purchase of his stud farm.

Asking my mother to go over the 'small print' with him, they slowly realised that the nominal amount he had hoped to receive had been swallowed up in the continuing legal fees. Sadly, there was no cheque for him to show his mates and in fact there remained an outstanding bill of around £30.

However, since the night of his British Legion speech, the news of Arthur's stud farm continued to circulate around Woking. And although, when later, he had tried explaining the outcome to his mates, and their mates, they never believed him. Moreover, complete strangers would sometimes buy him a drink, to ask if he had anything entered in next year's Classics.

# CHAPTER NINE

## *When the Red, Red, Robin*

Betting on football matches in the 1950s was, for me, a difficult occupation.

And it was not made any easier by being a National Serviceman in the RAF under the constant gaze of Corporal Buchan and Flt-Lt Ruggles. Especially as Ruggles, having perused my previous service record, had from day one made it his personal mission to thwart my gambling exploits.

Having been transferred from my position of orthopaedic clerk at RAF Hospital, Ely, to the Bristol University Air Squadron, my duties as a newly promoted Senior Aircraftsman, were to look after the records of students learning to fly light aircraft at nearby Filton Airport. As you can probably foresee, with an eye open for the sporting chance, it took little time for me to settle into the Bristol scene – dog racing at Knowle in the afternoons and then at Eastville (home of Bristol Rovers) in the evenings.

Strangely, when it came to betting on either Bristol City or Rovers, local bookies, pre-betting shops, would only take trebles. A rule, according to them, to make match-fixing difficult to profit from, but in reality hiding their profitable margins.

Whilst in the NAAFI one evening, I was introduced to the camp football raffle, a 'tanner a ticket' for the correct score. The match chosen was alternatively the Saturday home game of either Bristol City or Rovers. However, having drawn three blanks, I had to think again.

Late that evening, the list of scores was put up on the noticeboard. The game this week was Bristol City v Bournemouth at Ashton Gate. And, as the weather forecast for Bristol was 'bright and sunny', I thought it would be interesting to go along and add another name to my list of venues visited.

However, I must have a financial interest, otherwise, for this dyed-in-the-wool Woking fan, the game would come up short on my list of 'games to remember'.

So supporting the time-honoured maxim that, 'If you don't ask, you don't get,' I went over to the noticeboard to see who had drawn 1-0 and 2-0 City, my preferred choice of scores.

As the prize was more than my weekly wage, I could, having worked out the odds, hopefully tempt the ticket holders to part with their chance. Looking down the list, I quickly found 1-0. My heart sunk – Corporal Buchan, and then 2-0 – Corporal bloody Buchan again! My soul groaned.

After about ten minutes, time for me to sink my second Guinness, Corporal Buchan came into the NAAFI and, after ordering a drink, went to the noticeboard. Seizing my chance I stepped up alongside him.

'Any luck Corporal,' I enquired, guilelessly. His eyes ran over the list.

'Yes, as a matter of fact, I might have. In fact . . .' Buchan lent heavily on facts. 'Look, 1-0 and 2-0 City,' his honest Yorkshire face turning to smile in recognition.

'Would you like to sell one of them,' I proposed.

'How much for then, Church?'

So, trying to avoid the trap of being involved in yet another dodgy cash scam, I said, 'How about a bottle of whisky?'

Surprisingly, to me, he agreed and then asked me which score I wanted.

'Two-nil,' I replied. Buchan paused.

'No, I think you could be right. You take the 1-0 Church and I'll take the whisky.' And he did.

Arriving at Ashton Gate amongst a sea of red, the shed-end choir were already belting out '*When the red, red, robin goes bob, bob, bobbin* . . .', a nice change I thought from the over popular '*Goodnight Irene*' offered up by Rovers fans at Eastville.

For the inquisitive, this was a Third Division South match played at the end of the 1954-55 season. City were now top of the league,

*SAC Church on parade – second right*

83

largely due to the ability of John Atyeo, an England striker, who apart from five goals for England, went on to score 350 goals from 647 appearances for Bristol City, before retiring in 1966 – the epitome of a one club man.

Bournemouth, meanwhile, were lower mid-table, and sadly, it looked to me that Corporal Buchan had the more likely score.

At half-time, as I remember, there was no score.

Searching at a new ground for a lavatory and a cup of tea, in that order, is usually difficult for a newcomer. But, today, I was relatively fortunate, as the dilapidated lavatory stood cheek by jowl to the pie and tea stall. So joining the queue of 60 or 70 men and boys, I eventually entered the edifice, which resembled a wartime bunker.

Fifteen minutes later, the first part of the task completed, I joined the adjacent line for a much-needed cuppa. However, soon after the game restarted, chaos broke out when Atyeo banged in an early goal. The queues intermingled in a dash back to the action, causing damp trousers, not all from spilt tea.

Fortunately, being at the front of the queue, I had decided to stay put, but five minutes later, got a graphically described account of Atyeo's brilliant goal. One-nil to City and, if it would only stay that way, I would be in clover, at least until Eastville dogs on Wednesday night.

As is usual with this type of bet, the rest of the game was a torture every time either side got near the goal. And my fear of anyone scoring prompted one puzzled fan standing next to me to ask, 'Bloody hell Airman, which team are you supporting?'

Five minutes before the end, I decided to head for the exit to avoid the inevitable crush getting out. Then having just gone through the gate, I heard a roar.

'Oh, for heaven's sake,' I thought, and scrambled back to learn my fate.

'No, that John Atyeo's just hit the post, bloody near thing!'

'And so say all of us,' I muttered.

Back in the NAAFI at Filton that evening, I was happy to buy a round of drinks for all the regulars; Corporal Buchan had the good grace to say 'Well done,' and took part in the spirit of things.

However, midway through the evening, Flt-Lt Ruggles, conspicuous in civvies, popped in for a quick half, and, looking at the noticeboard came over to congratulate Buchan.

'Whose the lucky winner then?' he opened. 'Couldn't have happened to a more deserving chap.' Buchan put his chin forward and smiled.

'Thanks, it would have been nice,' he said wryly.

'Would have been,' Ruggles probed.

'Well actually, Church offered me a drink for the ticket, so I let him have it.'

'A drink,' Ruggles repeated.

'Well a bottle of whisky, actually.'

'A bottle of whisky,' Ruggles parroted. 'I might have known it,' he said in exasperation. 'Whenever there's a sniff of ready money, Church is always there; he's like a magnet. Do you know . . .' he continued.

I flinched, half expecting him to tell them of my mince pie and sherry swindle in the Officers Mess, but fortunately, a group of airmen on their fourth round of drinks irreverently interrupted him and brought him over a pint.

As the evening went on, he did appear to mellow, but just before 'Last orders please,' he loomed up alongside me to say 'You might think you have got away with it this time Church, but I'm watching you. Just remember, I'm watching you.'

Flt-Lt Ruggles did exactly that, and was a thorn in my side until, when not wishing to be left out of my infallible greyhound syndicate, he lost his money along with the rest of the squadron when the system crashed out one wet and windy night at Eastville. Fortunately, I was immediately transferred to a fire-fighting unit in Lancashire and never saw him again.

# CHAPTER TEN

## *The Red Head Shows Late*

'Look at that staircase Bert!' exclaimed Roy in disbelief. Roy and Malcolm stared up at the winding steps leading up to a first floor jazz club opposite the sea front at Brighton.

Having unloaded a full drum kit, a vibraphone, double bass, two saxes, a clarinet and my trumpet, we now faced the problem of getting them up a steep and narrow staircase.

The musicians, known as the Bon Accords, are our local modern jazz group who are combining a sea-front gig with a trip to Brighton races.

Bert is our PR man, who doubles on double bass – he's a tall, well-built, crew-cutted guy, in his late 20s, sporting the latest lapel-less blazer.

The band trusted Bert. He had previously engaged us as the support band to The Jazz Couriers, featuring Tubby Hayes and Ronnie Scott, and later, to Kenny Ball, when touring with his '*Midnight in Moscow*' hit.

However, today, the six members of the band, having squeezed into a Volkswagen van at Woking, now looked washed ashore on a busy Brighton pavement in the height of the season.

But, with good spirit, the six of us – including John, the leader/

driver, clarinet and tenor; Coleman, 'Look at the legs on that?', our virile alto sax, and myself, trumpet – all together pushed, pulled and manoeuvred all the instruments upstairs. Finally, we set up the music stands and sorted the arrangements, while Bert adjusted the microphones – all by noon.

A pub lunch was our first thought, with pints all round, before heading up the hill to the racecourse. This was Brighton Cup day in 1960; the track's principal meeting, with Lester Piggott and Scobie Breasley renewing their battle for champion jockey and Geoff Lewis, Jimmy Lindley and Willie Snaith all with choice rides.

Whilst Bert and I were well versed in the racing scene, none of the others had been racing before. So, a quick session on who was who and what was what, helped them understand a little.

Meanwhile, Coleman made a beeline for an attractive blonde barmaid he introduced to us as Sandy.

Although Malcolm, our cautious vibes player, reminded us that he couldn't afford to lose much, John said he was confident we would have a good day and in his enthusiasm queued up at the payout window to place his bet.

Brighton in summer was traditionally kind to favourite backers, so without more ado we pooled our resources, lumped on and, were rewarded with the first two winners – Flash Past 7-4 (Jimmy Lindley) and Black Game 6-5 (Scobie Breasley). After that, an air of confidence spread through our first-time punters.

Roy suggested that another time we go straight to the races and leave the instruments at home.

'I've made more money on the first two races than I expect to get from the gig. And next time, I wouldn't have to carry a drum kit upstairs!'

'It's not always like this, Roy,' I tried to explain, but by now, he was too busy counting his money to listen.

Due to the firm going, fields in these pre-watering days tended to be small. Even so 12 turned out for the Brighton Cup, won by the frequent course winner Illinois – Lester up and 7-1 – much to the delight of Bert, who collected again when Lester took the maiden race, on Noel Murless's Astrador.

Talking of maidens, no-one had seen Coleman since before the first race, so Roy and Malcolm, the more reliable members of the band, were sent on a recovery mission.

After three pints of lager, followed by whisky chasers and a vocal chorus of '*That's why the lady is a tramp*', Coleman, our smooth talking sax player, seemed to be getting considerable attention from Sandy behind the bar.

The modest efforts of Roy and Malcolm could do nothing to persuade Coleman to join us out on the track, and when Bert joined the party to splash some of his winnings, we all gave up hope, especially when Sandy's friend Laura – Shoreham's answer to Rita Hayworth – deftly moved in on Bert, and made herself comfortable in his prized blazer.

Catching a glimpse of the runners going to post, I pealed away, taking our leader, John, with me. Happy to avoid the booze-up and now determined to have a bet, he got onto the end of one of the queues for the Tote. However, in the rush, he had not only lost his racecard but, on getting to the front of the queue, could not remember either the name, or number of the horse he wanted to back.

'I do remember he wore a hood,' he explained pathetically to the young lady behind the wire grill.

While his frustration mounted, her expression drove him in desperation to turn to the impatient racegoers behind, shouting, 'Which horse is wearing a hood?' The exasperated queue chorused in unison, 'It's bloody Bucktail, and if you don't get a move on, none of us will be able to back it!'

Rushing to the rails, we could see only snatches of the race. However, when they stormed past us, a hooded horse led, amid a flurry of whips and a barrage of shouting.

John, flushed with excitement, sprinted past us to be first in line at the payout window, a strangely familiar territory to him.

Soon after, bitten by the bug and borrowing a racecard, he dashed off to the paddock.

The last race was a five-furlong sprint and whilst I had made money early on, I now needed another winner.

Putting ambition to caution, and by the way ambition won, I plumped for Fine Feathers, Scobie Breasley up, in a three-horse race with very tight betting. And mine 6-4 favourite.

As they came under orders, I rushed up to the nearest bookmaker's board, thrust the contents of my jacket pocket, less my trumpet mouthpiece, into his hand, and took the 6-4.

Backing Breasley was invariably a nail-biting affair, as he would always leave it as late as possible, and here he was, last of three, inside the final furlong. But I needn't have worried, as a moment later, he went cruising by to win easily by two lengths.

Quite a relief, and when I had recovered, I thoroughly enjoyed it.

More so than John, I think, who had splashed out on the second, Tune Time, because of the name.

Back to the bar, Coleman and Bert's party was going from good to better or, possibly worse, depending on whether you were thinking of that evening's gig.

Soon, the crowds were fleeing the racecourse, queues were forming at the bus stops, and Sandy was calling out 'last orders please'.

At this point, Laura went round kissing everybody and saying goodbye.

'Come on Bert, my glass is empty,' pleaded Coleman.

'Yeah, yeah, ok, ok, same again everyone?' Bert had no need to enquire. Fitfully rummaging through his trouser pockets, it suddenly hit him, Laura had left wearing his blazer!

I have to say, Bert looked desolate, particularly when having to go 'Dutch' for the last round. A true member of the 'cool school', he hadn't let on that, apart from his wallet, his coat contained the band's payroll for the night.

With two hours to kill before the gig, we found a decent café in the *Old Stein*, to soak up the afternoon's excesses with a choice of pies, chips and peas or the special, an Indian curry – a daring departure from their usual all-British menu.

John and Bert, meanwhile, ran through the playing order of our numbers and the order of solos. Although at best we were only semi-pro, our ambitions were high and most of the players were taking lessons from well-known jazz musicians. I would travel to the Jewish quarter of Whitechapel every Saturday morning, where Leon Calvert, lead trumpeter for the Johnny Dankworth band, gave me a grilling with endless scales, controlled breathing, and ballads – 'Play it nicely, Michael, stroke out the notes; pretend it's a woman!'

Finally, after selling me a hand-made copy of Maynard Ferguson's mouthpiece, he would run through his technique for high notes. Now this might have been a strong point for him, but I was more committed to the cool sound of Chet Baker and the West Coast Jazz scene. Even so, you don't protest when the guy is at the top of his trade, do you?

Incidentally, Leon's brother was Eddie Calvert, the trumpeter of the 'Oh Mein Papa' and 'Cherry Pink and Apple Blossom White' hits, that had previously dominated the pop charts.

The time had come to climb that staircase again, and a scattering of the Brighton youth had already arrived and were seated along the sides of the room. Bert adjusted the levels of sound and away we went

– '*Take The A Train*' – '*I'm Beginning To See The Light*' – followed by Dave Brubeck's '*Take Five*', with barnstorming choruses from Casanova Coleman swelling the floor.

It was about an hour later that we learnt the truth. Bert solemnly and with dignity, broke the news of our missing money. There were some long faces, especially from those desperately overdrawn at the bank. Roy wanted to know if either Coleman or Bert had got Laura's phone number, or even Sandy's would be a start.

The situation began to look desperate. Malcolm said it reminded him of the football taunt to away fans – 'All that way for nothing.' But just when our dejection looked set to ruin the second half of the show, a disturbance at the end of the room, involving a bouncer and a red head, brought in two familiar faces – Laura and Sandy. What a relief.

Neither had given any hint that they might be coming, but more to the point, Laura was wearing the blazer.

The word spread through the band like a forest fire, and after Bert recovered the envelope, to quell any fears he paid everyone out on the spot.

'Never been so pleased to see a red head, ever,' he said with passion.

Kicking off again with the exuberant '*C Jam Blues*', John gave everyone a chance to let off steam – it must have been infectious, for the floor resembled those early jazz movies with everyone jumping and jiving.

The club proprietor congratulated Bert for a swinging session and he promptly booked the band again for the following month.

At the end of the show, we had some decisions to make, or at least Bert and Coleman did. Fortunately, they stayed to help us down the stairs with the instruments; the vibraphone seemed more difficult going down than up, its tubular pipes clanking back and forth in discord.

Coleman and Bert then went into a discussion with the girls, the

*Michael on trumpet*

upshot being the four would go back to Sandy's one bedroom flat. A bit tricky, but Laura lived with her mum and dad, so no nonsense there!

On our way, wedged in the back of the van, between the double bass and the bass drum, I must admit I slept fitfully. However, the main thrust of my dreams was visiting many more jazz clubs close to racecourses – my twin passions.

Finally, John's voice broke my reverie, 'Come on Churchy, you're home, and don't forget your trumpet case.'

Undeterred, I replied, 'What would you say to a gig at Goodwood?'

# CHAPTER ELEVEN

## *The Treble Chance and Penny Points*

'**B**renda, it's the Pools man.'

'Oh no, I haven't done it yet; ask him to be a dear and come back in half an hour, would you?'

Brenda and John were regulars on my Friday night round and their modest permutation to find eight draws from ten matches, at an old penny a line, amounted to 3/9d, at this time, 1960, equal for many to around an hour's work.

In these pre-lottery days, the Treble Chance gave the man in the street a chance to dream – a £75,000 dream on a good week.

And so, I came back in half an hour to give them their chance to dream, along with the 30 to 40 others that I would collect from on this new housing estate just outside Woking.

It all seems such small beans now, but having scraped the barrel in all directions to put the deposit on our first house (a new three-bedroom semi – the cheapest new house on the market at the time), I desperately needed to earn a little extra. Ten per cent commission on these penny-staked pools was certainly little, but it was extra.

My first port-of-call on Friday nights was at our next-door neighbours, Nancy and Johnny. They too, like most of the estate, were first-time buyers. However, rather than supplement their income they would economise, a little drastically in our eyes – home-made soap, toothpaste rolled with a sardine key and of course home-brew beer and elderberry wine – a way of life really. Even so, they still found 18 pence for a small perm on Littlewoods.

Then, I would go over the road to one of the few detached bungalows, where Derek and Mildred lived. Older and better off than most of us, Derek dabbled in block perms, but it was always difficult to grasp his approach through the throbbing strains of '*Manuel and his Music of the Mountains*', which Mildred played endlessly throughout the day; neighbours forgivingly calling her Mildred of the Mountains.

However, one of the houses I enjoyed visiting the most was at the top of the hill. Bob Bickford, a *Daily Mail* journalist, would always have his bet ready and, when he knew I did graphs and forecasts for Kenwoods, he would occasionally get me to rough out something to accompany his next piece in the paper.

Of equal interest were the family of barn owls that he and his pretty, Swedish wife kept in their garage. Always looking for a challenge, he later made a pop record and sung on 'Top of the Pops'; a song that Pat and I dutifully promoted by singing when visiting the local shops. Thereafter, Bob wrote a weekly pop-music column, sometimes passing on to us the demo discs of recent chart busters.

One newlywed couple on my round were often passionately employed when I rang their bell. After one or two appearances at the door, showing signs of irritation and displaced clothing, they ever-after left their coupon in a flowerpot outside the front door.

One of the most harrowing experiences I had on those Friday nights came via the Oswalds and their child from hell. Wet from sleet and driving rain, I was kept waiting 20 minutes outside the door, while the mother filled in 18 single lines on the penny points, often stopping to ask me how I thought a particular match would end. Throughout the process their six-year-old, going on 16, made my wait even more unpleasant by staring hard and making gruesome expressions about eight inches from my face. To cap it all, when the time came, they couldn't find the money to cover the bet, so, 'Could we pay double next week?'

Actually, they could be quite thoughtful, for one week when they won about £4, they invited me in and gave me a bag of toffees.

However, one incident I shall never forget came when a couple got eight score draws in one line. The forecast in the Sunday papers was very good, in the region of £35,000.

The first I heard of it was on the Monday, when I met Audrey in the paper shop; her and Alf had spent the weekend making lists of how they were going to spend it.

'And of course we won't forget you. You've been brilliant coming out in all weathers.'

But my supervisor had no notification of a big winner, nor had I any record. This was a nightmare situation and I certainly had nightmares. The big question was – did I hand in the coupon or, had I lost it? My mind was a blank.

Audrey and Alf anxiously waited until the following Friday, but no telegram with the joyous news arrived. In fact, all the previous bon ami quickly evaporated as news of the couple's disappointment spread. And when I called into the shops on the estate, customers would suddenly go quiet and look away. My hard-worked round and its tiny income were crumbling away before my eyes.

Eventually, I plucked up courage and called on Audrey and Alf, mainly to clear the air, but also, hoping for some insight into the mystery.

'Well, look Michael, here's our half,' Audrey said, showing me the perforated copy coupon. 'I wrapped the two-bob-bit up in your half and put it on the window ledge in the hall, in front of the geranium, like I always do.'

She went out into the hall and pointed to the spot.

'You must have collected it,' she said in desperation.

Alf followed us out.

'I think you've over-watered that plant. I'll mop up the ledge,' he said testily.

And as he took away the geranium, so a neatly folded, but slightly soggy coupon containing the cash, appeared before our eyes.

Audrey and Alf looked first at me and then glowered hard at each other.

I hastily backed out of the door on legs weak with relief and, unsurprisingly, was never asked to collect their football coupon again.

I often look back at those 'hard-up' days, with wonder at my diligence in pursuing so little with so much effort. But I guess it was character building for the many trials and opportunities that lay ahead.

# CHAPTER TWELVE

## *Percy the Watchman*

U ncle Percy was a remarkably jovial fellow, despite having a leg
amputated after the Battle of the Somme, and then later, losing
the sight of one eye in a curious incident with a magpie. The latter,
finally put an end to his career as a watchmaker.

Percy was married to Mitzie, a small vivacious lady, now grown
buxom with age. She had often recalled her life as a chorus girl in
the music halls, before she became part of a novelty act – plates on
bamboo poles and that sort of thing – often footing the bill at the
Kingston Empire.

One Sunday, back in the mid-1960s, my wife Pat and I took a trip
on our Lambretta scooter to the Devil's Punchbowl – a well-known
beauty spot near Hindhead in Surrey. And, it was whilst hiking near
the top ridge I remembered that Uncle Percy, one of my maternal
grandmother's seven brothers, lived on the rim of the Punchbowl.

Eventually, for the path was both narrow and rough, we spotted a
bungalow above us. Venturing forth, I recognised Percy (eye-patch
and limp) out in the garden. I called out my name and introduced him
to Pat.

Very soon, we were seated around the fireplace with mugs of hot tea and buttered scones. Percy asked after his younger sister, Alicia Margaret (nan), who lived with my parents in the centre of Woking, while Mitzie took over Pat with questions about our new house in St Johns and our scooter, which we had parked a little way off. Our lively conversations, however, were punctuated by another voice – that of Henry, a large white parrot with a plumed head, who had settled on the back of Percy's chair. Alas, his profanities overtook our pleasantries and Mitzie swiftly returned him to his cage.

After a while, I told Percy of my new job at the Horserace Betting Levy Board and to my surprise, found him to be both interested and knowledgeable on racing. It seemed he had an old friend connected with Staff Ingham's yard in Headley and occasionally had a bet on 'something a bit special'.

Later, we bade farewell and promised to keep in touch. However, nothing ever came of it – that was, until two years later, when one night, quite late, I had a call from Percy.

'Michael, how are you? You remember us talking about Alec, a contact of mine with Staff Ingham at Thirty Acres Barn.'

'Yes,' I answered cautiously, wondering what was to come.

'Well, I've got some news of a smart two-year-old; finished second at Lingfield, and they are taking it to Windsor for the Star and Garter on Saturday.'

Continuing, his voice now wavered with anticipation. 'Would you like to be there and help me get some money on? Everything's got to be hush-hush you understand.'

'Yes, sounds exciting,' I replied. 'OK, meet me in the members bar under the grandstand before racing.'

'Percy, what's the name of the horse?'

'Oh yes, Watchman, good name for me eh? They've booked Geoff Lewis to ride.'

That Saturday, with Pat heavily pregnant with our second child, Sarah, and me a non-driver, I set out on the convoluted journey from Woking to Windsor racecourse – two trains, sometimes an hour apart, and a boat trip. The latter, a tourist attraction, had the ill-founded reputation for being quicker than the local bus.

Arriving 20 minutes before the first race, I quickly spotted Percy – county tweeds, eye-patch and walking stick. He told me he had spoken to Alec, and learned that Lewis had picked up a full book of rides and, apart from Watchman, Kitty's Grey, trained at Epsom by ex-jockey Kenny Gethin, 'should do the business'. Percy's passing shot as he went to the bar to order our lunch was, 'A monkey each on Watchman and I'll look after Kitty's Grey myself – alright.'

Whilst devouring the sausage sandwiches, Percy revealed he had recently sold a prize antique grandfather clock and, as yet, had not been able to bank the £1,500 in cash!

Just before three o'clock, Percy went off in search of a price against Kitty's Grey in the five-furlong maiden. He returned saying he had just had a small bet, but I noticed, meanwhile, the price had gone from 2-1 to 7-4.

Off and running, Hen-Pecked (far from Percy's predicament) went straight to the front and stayed there. However, soon after passing the post, the Tannoy announced haughtily, 'Objection to the winner by the second,' followed by 'stewards enquiry, stewards enquiry, please retain all betting tickets . . .'

Percy later learned that Geoff Lewis had objected to the winner for crossing and, in the jockey's words, 'cutting him up'.

In the ensuing delay, bookmakers took the opportunity to make a little extra or, as they would suggest, to allow punters to hedge their bets.

Percy felt he was now between 'the devil and the deep blue sea' – he could back Hen-Pecked and so negate most of his winnings, or do nothing and hope the result didn't reduce his intended stake on Watchman.

As the runners for the next race were going down, a crackly Tannoy interrupted with authority. 'Objection sustained, objection sustained … first Kitty's Grey, second Hen-Pecked, third …' The rest was drowned by Percy's cheering – more than usual for 'just a small bet' I thought.

Time for a celebratory drink, before Watchman's race at four o'clock.

Percy, flushed with excitement, insisted we both downed double whiskies before taking our monkeys to the bookies.

I knew there were only five runners, but the odds of 8-13 were disappointing; worse still, by the time we went forward, it had gone to 4-7. However, we got on at opposite ends of the line at exactly the same time to get £285 to £500 twice.

The race was a complete joy. After settling Watchman down, Lewis took him to the front and won in a canter by six lengths.

From then on, we planned to spend the rest of the afternoon in the bar, rather joyously, I'd hoped, but strangely, not so.

Suddenly, Percy caught sight of Alec hovering in the doorway and after quickly pushing back his chair, he said nervously, 'I need to disappear for a while; I think Alec's come to put the bite on me.'

'Perhaps I can help,' I feebly suggested, 'I'll, I'll, h-hold him up for a w-while,' I stammered. But Percy was in full flight now, leaving me to choose whether to hold-up or not to hold-up – that was the question.

Out of family loyalty to Percy, I made the effort and while Alec was furtively scanning the room for Percy, I approached.

'Excuse me,' I politely asked. 'Who won the last?'

'Err Watchman, Geoff Lewis up,' he replied.

'What price was that?' I persisted.

Alec, now looking agitated, ignored me, until . . .

'Haven't I seen you with Percy,' he questioned – he's got an eye-patch and a bit of a limp?'

Still giving Percy a chance to get away, I replied, 'Was that one eye patch or two?'

Alec looked angry and I thought at one point he was going to hit me, but he didn't.

'If you see him,' he said, scowling, 'tell him, Alec would like a word and, odds to a ton – tell him.'

'Bloody hell,' so that's why Percy wanted to scarper. Even so, a ton at 4-7 wasn't going to hurt him, but, if Kitty's Grey was part of the deal, then that was a different kettle. Meanwhile, Geoff Lewis continued his rich vein of form, winning the next race at 6-1 and so landing me three SP doubles. But was that another of Alec's tips, I wondered?

Needing to allow time for the situation to be resolved, I went out to the paddock and then watched a race from the terraces. When I returned to the members bar, Percy had got there before me and had continued with the double whiskies.

Strange as it may seem, this turned out to be a blessing for all concerned. For soon after insisting that he drove me back to Woking, Percy slumped forward onto the bar and passed out.

At that moment, I caught sight of Alec enquiring at the other end of the bar. Thinking quickly, I called him over. He surely couldn't put the finger on Percy in this state and it might defuse an ugly confrontation.

'Is he alright?' Alec enquired, looking down at an unconscious Percy.

I gave him a look of disbelief.

'We've got to get him home,' I said.

'You knew him after all then,' Alec said, revising his take on the situation.

'Who, Percy?' I retorted, still hoping to buy some time.

In the end, I came clean with Alec and to my surprise, he came clean with me.

'Look, I don't know your connection, but Percy and I go back a long way. Leave him to me, I'll run him home.'

'But why was he worried about paying odds to a £100?' I asked.

'No, that wouldn't bother him. He's been desperate to avoid me because he knows he sold me a fake antique grandfather clock – the bloody thing's quartz.'

I helped Alec drag Percy back to his car, Percy suspended between us with his arms drooped round our necks.

After propping him up in the back seat, Alec said, 'Don't worry Michael, I'll get him home alright.'

I was in no position to argue, but I dare not tell Alec that not only had Percy won around one and a half grand, but he also had his pockets stuffed with the fifteen hundred that Alec had given him for the clock!

The following day, I telephoned Mitzie to find out if Percy got back all right.

'Oh he's fine, thank you,' she said breezily. 'He's out celebrating with Alec at the moment,' and put the phone down.

Celebrating, celebrating – no mention of the clock, and sadly, there never was, because to this day, I never saw or heard from either Percy, Alec or Mitzie, ever again.

# CHAPTER THIRTEEN

## A Visit to Scotland

Packing our battered old Austin Cambridge estate with two adults, four children and all that would feed and amuse them for the journey wasn't easy. We had an invitation to stay with old friends in their new house in Paisley, near Glasgow, so an early start from Woking that Saturday was very important.

Pat, my wife, the only driver, had driven long journeys before, including taking the family camping in the south of France. So this, even in the late summer of 1973 was not viewed as daunting, until we passed the signs for Coventry, when the radiator temperature gauge went into the red.

Pulling into a garage, we were told that we needed a new thermostat, but they didn't have the one we needed. So, after waiting half an hour for the radiator to cool down and filling every container with water, we set off with hope, rather than confidence.

Fifty miles on and we were back in trouble. At this point, we decided to phone the AA and waited, and waited. Eventually they arrived. Unable to replace the thermostat, their best advice was to allow them to tow us back 50 miles to a garage that would open on Monday. No thanks.

And so, we limped on, 30-odd miles at a time, sometimes less, with long intervals; the children fallen asleep, exhausted with asking: 'Are we nearly there?'

Finally, we got into Paisley at around 2 a.m. the following morning, to be stoically greeted by our friends, Desmond and Elaine, who had kept a saucepan of hot broth simmering on the cooker.

A day or two later, when all had recovered, the big garden equipped with swings, slide and a climbing frame provided a happy environment for the eight children – each family exactly matching two boys and two girls, aged four to nine.

Meantime, after settling in, Tom, a wizard mechanic and a good neighbour of Desmond's, replaced the thermostat, checked our radiator and gave all the hoses the once over – marvellous.

Shown the sights of Paisley, we visited the Museum and Art Gallery and St Mirin's R.C. Cathedral, whose plain sandstone exterior gave it a definite Scottish feel. However, it didn't take long for my sporting preferences to come through. So on the Wednesday, they very kindly arranged a trip to Ayr, where, while the two families visited the sea and shops, I went to the races.

Ayr racecourse had a particular fascination for me, since this was where my grandfather, Ernest, would sometimes bring the whole family on holiday. On one such occasion, when he was a little in debt to a racecourse bookmaker, some unscrupulous heavies came in the night to loosen the wheels on his spanking new Sunbeam tourer.

The next morning, while driving off to meet his mistress, the car careered off the road at high speed, miraculously only damaging the bumper and bonnet – just one of the many colourful stories told about Ernest.

Today, bright, but windy – I think it's always windy at Ayr – I patiently waited for the third race and my nap of the day – Black Douglas.

A course and distance winner and due for a win, he was trained by Jack Ormston. Jack had been a famous speedway rider back in the

1930s, but had now successfully taken up training racehorses from Richmond in Yorkshire.

Chasing round the bookies' boards, I grabbed the disappearing 6-1 for a tenner and then climbed the terraced steps for a better view.

Last into the straight, his jockey, Alec Russell, was forced to deliver him late, up the outside. It looked desperately close – 'Photograph, photograph.'

I waited. Should I back the other one at Evens to save my stake? I dithered. Yes, perhaps I should. However, before I could get to the bookies the Tannoy announcement, wind buffeted, blurted, 'First, Black Douglas ... distance a short head.'

Walking back from collecting my winnings, I was struck by a very tall man, busy with his Raceform. He was unusually dressed for the occasion – all in black, overcoat buttoned to the neck and a Homburg hat, like those featured in *The Godfather*. Later, when he came into the bar he had unbuttoned his coat to show a glimpse of a dog collar. He then ordered a large scotch and continued to bury his head back in his Form Book, scribbling notes in the margin – nice to see someone taking it seriously, I thought.

After racing, the family picked me up outside the main entrance and, having had a good day, we invaded a fish and chip parlour to place an order for four adults, topped with onions and gherkins and eight junior helpings!

Although sporting, in the wider sense of the word, Desmond and Elaine could not be pressed into going to Shawfield dogs on Saturday night. And when Pat and I got there, we could see why.

Whatever it had been in its heyday was hard to imagine, but if I said there were 250 people there, I would be exaggerating.

The card was made up of eight, five-dog races (trap 6 always vacant) – all handicaps and all over the standard four bends. This was fine from the management's point of view, as they could keep going with a minimum pool of greyhounds, just mixing and matching them with individual handicaps of up to 13 yards. However, for those used to the London scene, having confidence in the programme's adjusted times needed a leap of faith.

Sadly, I never did master it and after three failed attempts to back a winner, I was grateful to get my money back after a 'no-race'.

Retreating to the track's cafeteria, I noticed with some surprise, away in the far corner, with an outlook over the track, the black Homburg hat.

After ordering a couple of hot-dogs, and they really were hot, we tried the local Bovril brew, a known delicacy at that time in Glasgow. I then related to Pat how I had seen the 'Homburg' at Ayr races a few days before. Watching him from a distance, his old leather despatch case was in constant use, crammed with what looked like a hundred or more previous programmes. Had he worked out his own rating system I wondered? Whatever he was doing he was totally absorbed.

Sunday with our friends consisted of early morning Mass, en masse, followed by Desmond's three-hour supervision of a Sunday roast, during which the prime Aberdeen Angus joint was under a 360-degree surveillance.

The family feast, finally washed down with an adults-only vintage port, was a welcome surprise. However, this was topped with the announcement that Desmond had got tickets for the Celtic v Sunderland match at Parkhead on Monday evening.

Parkhead was packed, lively and full of noise. The powerful Tannoy blasted out Elton John's '*Saturday Night's Alright For Fighting*', while we located our seats near the halfway line.

For those readers not then born, Celtic, under the management of Jock Stein, had won the Scottish League Championship for the previous eight years. Sunderland, meanwhile, had recently charmed the nation by winning the FA Cup final whilst still in the old Division 2, beating Leeds 1-0. I was particularly charmed, having backed the correct score at odds of 16-1.

Looking at the programme some names jumped off the page – Jinky Johnstone for Celtic, Sunderland's diminutive five feet four inch captain Bobby Kerr, and of course, Ian Porterfield, who scored their winning goal at Wembley. But, however exciting the game might have been, and Sunderland won 2-1, the lasting memory for Pat and I was the continual passing up and down of supporters clutching handfuls of meat pies and mugs of hot Bovril. It started half an hour before the game and continued, without a break, until the final whistle.

It always amazes me how quickly football grounds empty. Ten minutes later, we were outside on the pavement, when my eyes were drawn to a tall figure in a black Homburg, crossing the road and hugging a despatch case.

By the time we got back to Paisley the children were in bed. Desmond was about to pour us a nightcap when there was a knock on the door. It was Tom, the mechanic. They were having a party a few doors away, and would we like to join them for a wee drink or two?

Desmond and Elaine declined, but said to us, 'No, you must go.

He's a great sport. You can tell him about the game.' So we did.

We hadn't been there long, when, after discussing the Celtic match with Tom, he introduced us to a Father Green.

'Please, just call me Perry,' he said. A very tall, round-faced man, with a pleasant smile shook my hand. Tom shepherded us together and painted the picture.

'Perry and I go back a long way, Michael. And I'm sure he won't mind me telling you, he's quite an expert on some sports, and he likes a bet,' Tom said with a twinkle in his eye, continuing: 'Many years ago at his seminary . . .' But at this point, Perry interrupted, 'No, no, no, Tom, get these fine people another drink.'

However, eventually, Perry was persuaded to tell the story.

'You see Michael, at the seminary, the abbot was convinced that I loved betting more than my vocation. And when the word got around I had won £200 in a late night poker school, he not only suspended me, but asked me to reconsider my future. It was a blow, I can tell you. But despite the abbot accusing me, quite rightly, of having one foot in each camp, if you know what I mean, I could never let go of the faith.'

Tom, bursting to interrupt, said: 'Ah, but you stuck it out, didn't you Father, and got there in the end. He's been the godfather of all our children, yer know.'

'Good heaven's is that the time,' said Perry, looking at his watch.

'Never mind the time, have another wee dram,' pleaded Tom.

But no, he had to go and Tom saw him to the door, finally, calling out behind him, 'Father, don't forget your Homburg.'

# CHAPTER FOURTEEN

## *Father Green and the Portrait of Lillie Langtry*

There was a sharp rat-tat-tat at the door. Emily opened it and was faced with a tall unshaven man of about 50. He wore a grubby, belted raincoat and carried a paper bag containing a geranium.

'Would you take this in and give it to Father Green,' he said, pushing it up to her clean pinafore.

'I can't come in for the minute, but here, take my calling card and tell him, with luck, I'll be back in 20 minutes.'

'Who was that?' Perry Green called out, his study door ajar.

'A bit of a mystery if you ask me Father. Look, he's given you a geranium in a pot and said he might be back soon. He didn't sound all that sure though. See, he's got a calling card – very posh. More than I could say about him – looked like he'd come from the down and outs.'

'Now, now, Emily, what have I told you, we are all God's children.' Father Green paused and then read out the card – 'James O'Neil, Investment Manager. James O'Neil,' he repeated.

'I wonder what's brought Jimmy back after all this time,' he murmured to himself.

Then joyfully he said to Emily, 'Well, it's a beautiful geranium – cardinal red, I shouldn't wonder. Would you find me a saucer to put under it and I'll keep it on my desk. It'll brighten the place up.'

Emily had kept house for Father Green for over a year now, since he'd moved down from Scotland to become a relief priest covering London's East End. Emily, an earnest, but attractive middle-aged widow, said she missed the company and once Perry had learned that she was from a racing family, he told her he thought she would fit in well, and she did.

The visit of Jimmy O'Neil seemed to have unsettled Perry. He gazed out of the window, trying to remember the details of their agreement and then, up to the signed framed photograph of Lillie Langtry that was a part of it. He remembered he had accepted the photograph as some sort of collateral against a loan to get Jimmy started. Market Gardening it was then, but for how much?

The story was that Jimmy's grandfather, Tommy, was in the theatre, *The Princes*, actually, in Shaftesbury Avenue. And at that time, Lillie Langtry, who numbered the Prince of Wales among her admirers, was playing Cleopatra in *Antony and Cleopatra*.

As part of Tommy's many and varied jobs, he would often be called upon to run errands for her, sometimes with a bet. Anyway, at the end of the run, she gave Tommy a signed photograph as a keepsake. Tommy had it framed and when he died, somehow it got passed down to Jimmy, who, as Father Green observed, had certainly made good use of it since then.

Later that day, there was a series of heavy knocks at the door. Emily looked through the side window – it was Jimmy.

'Father Green, would you open the door to your man Jimmy – it looks like he's been drinking.'

Jimmy stood on the front step, swaying, rolled up newspapers in one coat pocket and a bottle of whisky poking out of the other.

'Come in won't you?' invited Perry. 'It's been such a long time. Thanks for the geranium by the way; I love geraniums. Let me take your raincoat.'

Perry ushered Jimmy into his study, where Jimmy sat down heavily on the easy chair, narrowly missing Perry's resting Homburg.

'I've been meaning to call you for some time Father, but thought I'd wait until I had some good news.'

'Emily,' Perry beckoned, 'would you be kind enough to make us two strong coffees – black.'

*Lillie Langtry as Cleopatra*

'Good news you say?' Perry returned to the conversation.

Jimmy cast his eyes upwards to the portrait.

'Ah, she was a lovely lady and a fine actress, Gramps would say ...'

Father Green cut in. 'Good news you said?'

'Oh yes, well, you remember that I played the ponies a bit, same as you Father. Well today at Epsom there was a filly running – Lily Langtry – spelt different but, what a coincidence.'

Gulping the coffee, he continued, 'The form looked good; Richard Fox up and bottom weight. Silly really, but I thought of Gramps and the picture and had to back it and ...'

Once again, Jimmy's eyes drifted up to the portrait.

'And,' Father Green pressed.

'Oh yes, and she won, by six lengths. I heard it in the betting shop just along the street. Five to one the price – very fair – and so I've come to pay you back.'

Jimmy pulled a wad of notes out of his jacket pocket and began to count ...

'A hundred and forty, a hundred and fifty, there we are, payment in full.'

Perry was astonished. He had never thought he would see the money again, but, as his calling reminded him – trust and keep faith.

'I suppose you'll be wanting the portrait back now?' Perry enquired, sadly. For it would leave not only a space on the wall, but the darkened area around the space would remind him of where it had been.

'Well I was coming to that,' said Jimmy, tentatively.

'You see, I've had some business cards printed,' he reached to his inside pocket.

'Yes, you left one, thank you,' replied Perry.

'And what I'm planning on doing,' Jimmy continued, 'is taking an ad in the *Sporting Chronicle* and setting up as a tipster – three tips for

£2 – cash in advance, cheque or postal order. The punters, or clients if you like, would phone me each day for the selection.'

'Sounds a bit risky,' Perry commented, 'but good luck to you!'

'It's a great opportunity Father, and I'd like you to come in with me,' enthused Jimmy.

Father Perry shifted uneasily in his chair.

'All I need,' Jimmy continued, 'is £100 to get started, get a telephone connection, some accounts ledgers and book a few ads in the *Chronicle*. Oh, and you could keep the portrait of Lillie Langtry for collateral – like as before!'

Father Green gave a sigh. 'Oh well,' he said, philosophically, 'I've got £50 more than I had this morning; I've met up with an old friend and I've got a beautiful geranium.'

It was three weeks before Jimmy called again. His landlady didn't want another phone in her house and wouldn't let him use her private phone for business purposes. She had also suggested that if he had got any spare money he could keep his rent up to date.

After that, he had tried working from the public phone box; however, his continual presence in the booth regularly upset locals and those wishing to make a quick call.

On the bright side, the response from the adverts had been good. He had six regular clients and what's more he had tipped them a few winners.

He had called on Father Green today, to ask him a small favour – they were partners after all.

'Ah Jimmy, nice to see you again. How's your tipping business?'

'Our tipping business,' Jimmy corrected.

'We're doing fine Father, tipping winners and building up OUR business a treat,' he emphasised.

'Just one thing, and I thought I would call on you for your suggestions.'

Father Green braced himself.

'Unfortunately, I have to go into hospital for a few days; two weeks tops.'

'Nothing serious I hope,' Perry enquired.

'Oh no, nothing like that, but we need to keep the telephone calls coming. So, and it's only about six or seven calls a day, between 10 and 12 in the morning usually.'

'How will I know which horse to tell them?' Perry asked, going along with it thus far.

'Oh well, for the time I'm away, just give them Newsboy's nap and The Scout's nap on alternate days – you can't go far wrong there. Would you do that for us Father?'

'I'm afraid for professional reasons, you understand, I daren't. But if Emily agrees and you offer her a little bonus, she may well say yes.'

Amazingly, Emily did agree – even said it would be fun – and she hastened to order the *Daily Mirror* and the *Daily Express*.

After the first week, the naps were breaking even, with two or three winners covering the losers. However, Father Perry, initially cautious, gradually increased his interest in the selections, and after spending the early mornings avidly studying the form, he began to replace the newspaper naps with his own.

There were now around a dozen calls every morning and occasionally, Emily would give someone seeking the times of confessions a runner in the 2.30.

After two weeks without word of Jimmy's return, Father Green telephoned the hospital.

'Jimmy O'Neil, you say. I'll check the Medical ward's record.'

Perry could hear the nurse turning the pages of the record book.

'Oh yes, here it is, "Removal of gangrene appendix."'

Suddenly her voice changed. 'Are you a relative?' she asked.

'No, I'm a priest, a friend of his.'

'Well, I'm very sorry to tell you that Mr O'Neil died during the operation, there were unexpected complications. We were unable to trace any relative to inform. I am so very sorry,' she concluded.

Father Perry sat in his study in a daze, his sadness for his lonely friend clouding the issue of what to do next – all those phone calls every day, and the money side to sort out too?

He had to admit that Emily was so enjoying the punters' conversation that the cleaning and the cooking, particularly the latter, had been put on the back burner. And, on top of that, his own burgeoning interest was sure to cause problems.

The next morning, Emily pulled a face at Perry and said embarrassedly, 'It's Bishop Franks for you.'

'Good morning Perry, how are you?'

'I'm very well, thank you your grace.'

'I say, what was that your housekeeper said about Lochnager for the July Cup?'

'Oh, Emily's just been reading the paper – she sometimes gets carried away with the sports pages.'

'I hope your right Perry. I'd hate to think you were getting involved in betting again.'

'As if I would, come on now Bishop, have faith.' He caught sight of himself in the reflection of the window and hurriedly sat down.

'Anyway Perry … are you still there Perry?'

'Yes, yes, go on.'

'I was telephoning to say, I will be visiting you and your neighbouring parishes in the next week or so and I would like to drop in. I'll ring before I arrive though. Don't want to call at an inopportune moment,' he said chuckling.

Inevitably, a week later, Bishop Franks phoned to say he would be there in an hour.

'Oh, I am very sorry your grace,' apologised Emily, 'He has gone to Lourdes. Sudden like, yes I know. It was depression really. His friend died unexpectedly you see and left him with a few problems.'

'After Christmas you say,' Emily lightened. 'Yes, that'll be fine. He just needs a good break.'

She put down the phone and breathed a deep sigh. It rang again immediately.

'Hello, yes, it's LAMBS TALE in the three o'clock at Newbury, Willie Carson's up.'

Then, glancing behind her, called out, 'Perry, put the kettle on, this is thirsty work.'

'Shan't be long,' he replied, 'just straightening the portrait of Lillie.'

# CHAPTER FIFTEEN

## *First at the Post*

The first issue of the *Racing Post* was published on Tuesday, 15 April 1986.

The staff had been recruited over the previous six months, some headhunted, but most through a series of interviews from full mailbags of applications. My own appointment for the position of accountant had been surprisingly achieved from a field of 53, and in the weeks that followed, I thought I had died and gone to heaven – having an office on the top floor meant regularly passing the time of day with the likes of Sir Peter O'Sullevan, Lord Oaksey and Brough Scott.

The first editor, Graham Rock (later of Pasternak fame), had put together a professional and polished team of journalists and sub-editors from *Timeform*, *The Sporting Life*, the late *Sporting Chronicle* and from the ranks of the national dailies.

Impressively, among the hundred or so staff, there were a number of devotees in editorial who, having already watched all the races on TV that day, would take home the videos to analyse them again that evening.

As in any gathering of dedicated sporting aficionados, eccentrics were well represented, as were those walking the tightrope of life; one man was reputed to be living in a room without furniture, but kept his greyhound books in the refrigerator, while another came to work in shorts and mountain boots whatever the weather.

There was also the young man who ran up a large bookies' bill and then disappeared, it was thought, to Australia – one aspect of a betting life.

The girls, however, came from different stock. A few, a generation before, may well have been presented as debutants, but in the main, most were well-educated and well-groomed secretaries. Those in advertising tended to be a bit worldlier, but despite the dizzy pace of life, they knew how to keep their wheels on the road.

After producing several dummy-run editions there was great relief and a sense of achievement when the paper finally went live.

Sonic Lady, featured on the front page of the first edition, duly won the Nell Gwyn that day, while Dancing Brave took the Craven Stakes two days later.

After the Guineas meeting, due to the scheduled demolition and rebuilding of the Rowley Mile members stand, the remainder of the Newmarket fixtures that year were transferred to the July course, including both the Cambridgeshire and the Cesarewitch.

Later, that October, with the staff settled in and the Post's circulation growing month on month, a camaraderie had built up, and nowhere more so than in the advertising and bloodstock departments, where around ten staff, hell bent on making their monthly targets, would as a diversion avidly discuss the merits of the big-race candidates.

Landing the 'Autumn Double' had always been an ambition of mine and although my previous Cesarewitch winners included Avon's Pride, Grey Of Falloden and Cider With Rosie, all at good prices, I had never been able to double them with the Cambridgeshire winner.

About a week before the Cambridgeshire, I put together four £3 win ante-post doubles – two in each leg – Dallas 14-1 and Tremblant at 10-1 in the Cambridgeshire, with Orange Hill at 33-1 and what turned out to be a non-runner in the Cesarewitch.

Watching the Cambridgeshire at home on TV, Luca Cumani's Dallas, ridden by Ray Cochrane, scooted home inside the final furlong, to win by half a length from Power Bender, while my other selection, Tremblant, ran well to finish fourth.

The days that followed had a sustained expectancy as my small bet had progressed to a useful £45 going on a 33-1 shot. And since our son Shaun had entered Cambridge University and was living in local digs, I decided to make a day of it by visiting him before going on to Newmarket. As it was, he came too and started out with a party of friends.

'What's all this about Orange Hill?' they asked.

'Well, it's just that it's the second leg of an 'Autumn Double' bet that I've being trying to win since I was a tiny tearaway.'

'Has it got a chance?'

'Should we back it?'

The questions came thick and fast and I guessed that Shaun had told them that I worked at the *Racing Post*.

Anyway, later, when we met up with them again on the racecourse, they had all bet a pound or two on Orange Hill, who by that time had shortened to 20-1.

It was a good card that day and getting to the back of the long grandstand, we saw the gallant filly Triptych win the Champion Stakes in style from Celestial Storm.

Too nervous to go to the paddock for the Cesarewitch, I stayed high up in the stands. Twenty-five runners went to post, with Misrule the 11-2 favourite, while my filly, Orange Hill, was not in the first ten in the betting. As they cantered to post, I zoomed in on my dark green colours.

The long awaited 'They're Off,' reverberated along the course. But with all the excitement I was having difficulty in keeping my binoculars steady. Although I thought I spotted her about three furlongs out, seemingly going well, she then suddenly appeared in trouble and was shuffled back. I lowered my glasses – oh well, it was not to be.

Then a furlong out, I heard the commentator mention Orange Hill. Scanning the leaders, I saw a horse in dark green silks. This one with a black cap – not the one I had been following.

What's more, she went into the lead and with Richard Fox working away with only 7st 9lb, she looked to be staying on – just.

Both Marlion and Misrule closed to finish alongside and I feared there may have been some bumping – or was it just my heart?

I ran down to the winner's enclosure for a closer look – then waited. Would there be a stewards enquiry? But no, Fox looked happy and was chatting to trainer Jeremy Tree. The 'weighed in' was called and I raced off to find the telephones, which in these pre-mobile days, were strangely housed under a row of thatched umbrellas.

'Hello Pat, Orange Hill won! Wonderful, yes I know. Look,' I continued, 'would you do me a favour, go down to Thomas Cook's and book flights to Vancouver for the family? We are going to make that overdue trip to see your brother.'

About an hour later, having missed the next two races, I met up with Shaun and his mates in the bar at the top of the stand. In their effort to strike while the iron was hot, I was inevitably asked, 'Who's going to win the last?'

David Elsworth was running Perfect Timing; could she be the third four-year-old filly to win that afternoon? Her task looked difficult with 9st 11lb, but she did have Steve Cauthen aboard. However, what

*Orange Hill winning the 1986 Cesarewitch*

tipped the balance for me was her dam's sire, Indigenous, still held the world record over five furlongs – albeit over Epsom's downhill run, on firm ground, and with the wind behind him!

So having explained my careful, but probably flawed reasoning, they all headed off to the bookies' boards like men possessed – taking my modest tenner with them.

Having already witnessed the miracle of landing the Autumn Double, to see Cauthen take up the running in the final 150 yards and win at 8-1 seemed predestined.

Later, Shaun's friends memorably hailed me as the best father a chap could wish for, and made me promise to tell them when I was next going to Newmarket.

Back at the *Racing Post* the following Monday, word got around that 'Churchy has had a big win'.

At lunchtime, we celebrated cheerily with a few beers. Even editor Graham Rock put his head in, 'Well done Churchy – first class.' Then with a broad hint of irony added, 'If Adrian Cook (Diomed) ever goes sick, I might just be in touch.'

Actually getting my hands on the dosh, however, took a little longer. Going into the local Coral's, I was told, 'Sorry we don't keep that much in the till; security, you know. Can you come back in an hour?' This I did.

However, the week before an alert had gone around that there were some dud £50 notes in the area. So, when I eventually got paid out with 30 of them, plus a few tenners, I conscientiously began to hold them up, one by one, to the light.

Meanwhile, some of the senior *Racing Post* staff had come into the shop and were standing in line behind me. Soon, two of them started a whispered count . . . 'Eleven hundred, twelve hundred,' and so on, until eventually they filled the shop with their chant.

I slipped away discreetly, but they never let me forget that day – as if I would.

# CHAPTER SIXTEEN

## *Snowball*

To start with, it was a blustery day: intermittent showers and blasts of wind that would send plastic bags scurrying through the streets of tourist-laden Lyme Regis.

This was our family holiday and, ensconced in a 1920s cottage a mile or two out of town, we had come in seeking a diversion from the weather.

As was usual on these occasions, the ladies – Pat, my daughters Sarah and Mia, and my granddaughter Daisy – explored the local shops, while my son-in-law Gareth and I made for the trade fair and half-price book sale taking place in the Town Hall.

And, as the wind blew and the rain rained, so the prospect of rummaging through old books and prints grew ever more attractive.

However, after 20 minutes of looking at old *Rupert* annuals, 1950s film star magazines and a collection of Bing Crosby records, it felt like we had seen enough.

Nevertheless, the continuous rain outside caused us to prolong the experience. And it was soon after taking in the relief of 'two coffees and two slices of fruit cake, please', that Gareth spotted a small collection of prints.

Flicking through for anything sporting, I came across what looked like an antique print of a white greyhound in the style of a steel engraving.

Entitled blandly, 'The Greyhound', the dog, elegantly drawn, stood in an open field against a threatening sky. However, being printed off-centre with a hand-drawn border, on an unnecessarily large sheet of paper, I would at this point have normally said: 'Let's go'. But, catching the minute writing in the corner, 'Published October 15th, 1798,' I enquired as to the price?

'No idea mate,' was the encouraging reply from an ex-serviceman rearranging his selection of military cap badges.

'Fred's gone down the pub. He'll be back in an hour,' he added, helpfully.

Then, suddenly, Gareth spotted a card: 'All prints reduced to £5 each.'

Rejoining the women folk in a local pub for lunch, we studied with dubious appreciation the artistic stained glass windows depicting the historic tortures and public hangings at Taunton, before placing our order.

Eventually, I showed them my print. The reception was mild, bordering on the indifferent, until Pat, in a veiled critique, said, 'Another print. Where do you think that one's going?'

Back at home, I found a small black frame and with permission, hung it in the hall under 'Henry V – at Agincourt', appropriate I thought, remembering Harry's 'I see you stand like greyhounds in the slips, straining upon the start'.

Three weeks later, the print had now settled to the back of our minds. That was until Alf Simmonds arrived.

THE GREYHOUND.

Alf, a heating engineer, who had visited us about a year ago to service our gas boiler, was now called in to investigate the violent banging noises in the central heating system.

Alf, by no means a friend of the family, brought us together and with a grave expression and much sucking of the teeth, related, that, as he put it, 'Your war-time boiler has passed away noisily and is awaiting it's successor.'

It was groans all round, while Alf, going into the hall, made a series of phone calls out of earshot. 'Let me put it this way, expect a bill of £1,950, and you won't be disappointed,' he said, cheerfully, on his return.

We reluctantly agreed. Then, just as he was leaving, he seemed magnetically drawn to the print of the greyhound in the hall.

'That picture of the white greyhound; my grandfather must have had the original,' he said.

'I remember looking at it as a kid, when I went to see him. Gramps was very fond of coursing and once had a nomination for the Waterloo Cup,' he recalled with pride.

'I've just remembered the dog's name – Snowball.'

'How interesting,' I responded. 'I can look that up for you.'

'No, no, don't bother. It was definitely Snowball, I remember Gramps saying he was the champion greyhound around 1800, unbeatable, he was. It's all flooding back to me now.'

He drew back to reappraise the situation. 'How old is that print?' he challenged.

'I can't remember,' I said hesitantly. 'I think the date it was published is in the corner. It's a bit small, I'll get my glasses.'

'No, that's alright,' replied Alf, 'my eyes are good. In the corner, you say, let's see . . . 1798. There that proves it, it must be Snowball.'

'Well done,' I encouraged, as Alf positively glowed with pride.

Two weeks passed before Alf returned with the new Potterton boiler and, after a day of much clanking and more sucking of teeth the job was almost done.

Alf partook of his afternoon sandwiches in the hall, mesmerised by the image of Snowball. Re-emerging with an expectant look, he said: 'The bill, by the way is £1,950, but if you let me have the print of Snowball, I'll make it £1,900.'

'The bloody cheek,' I thought and in response said, 'We don't actually know that it is Snowball.'

'Oh, it's Snowball alright, it's definitely Snowball.'

'Well,' I paused.

'Look,' he interrupted. 'Prove it's not Snowball and I'll do the job for a grand – if you can't, the print's mine. How's that for a bet – you're supposed to be a gambling man!'

In the end, I agreed. It seemed the only way to keep him quiet and in reality, the odds looked attractive – £950 to a £5 print – exactly 190-1.

'I tell you what,' I said, going along with the sporting nature of the deal. 'Give me 24 hours of research, come round this time tomorrow, I'll have your money ready, in cash, either £1,950 or a grand and, if you're right, you can keep the print as a memento of the occasion.'

Alf laughed, 'You're a real sport Michael. It's been a pleasure working for you.'

The following afternoon, there was a sharp knock on the door.

'Alf's here,' called out Pat from the kitchen.

Alf bounded in.

'Your money's ready Alf.'

'Ah, thanks, all of it, I hope?' he queried.

'Yes, just come and look at this Alf,' I said, holding a printout from the Greyhound Data website.

'You were right about Snowball being the champion courser. You see,' I said, pointing to the printout, 'he was born in 1796, and owned and bred by Major Topham. It says here, that he won four cups and 30 matches, including the Malton Cup in 1798, so that ties up with the date on the print.'

Alf was a picture of satisfaction, rubbing his hands at the history of his white greyhound.

'The only trouble is,' I said slowly, **'Snowball was black!'**

For the reader's interest, to this day, the boiler is working fine. And the print of the white greyhound still hangs in the hall – name unknown.

# CHAPTER SEVENTEEN

## *One of Each Number*

One night, Cliff, a neighbour of ours, who was head teacher at a local school, came to ask Pat and I if we would support a fundraising 'Race-Nite' at his school. We said yes.

Pat and I had some experience of running Race-Nites for Woking Football Club, where sometimes the whole family would sell tickets for the tote, seated behind trestle tables with tills filled with change. I would add up the total tickets sold and calculate the win dividend.

Conscious of the fact that at Woking, many of those attending were habitues of Sandown Park and Wimbledon dog track, I would not burden them with the 50 per cent tote retention usually reserved for Race-Nites. My philosophy was that a 30 per cent take out was ample and therefore at least a few punters would go home winning and so spread the news of a good night out.

When we arrived at Cliff's school, early fortunately, it was already crowded. It had been difficult enough to park, but now, finding a seat looked even harder. Just then, I caught sight of Cliff.

'Pat, Michael, glad you got here in good time. I've saved you seats at my table, at the back, near the projector.'

We put our bottles of wine on the table – two for us and two for the raffle, while Pat brought out two wine glasses – with four children of school age we were old hands at school event procedure.

'Sorry you've had to bring your own drinks, but we don't hold a licence,' Cliff dutifully apologised. Then brightening, said, 'There's to be an auction, you know. I don't know if I told you?'

'Yes, we brought some dough – sounds exciting,' I enthused.

Cliff continued, 'I've got my Maths master to run the tote, they sent him a pack for 100 punters, forecasts and all.'

'What's the takeout?' I enquired, perhaps rather too casually, in an attempt to mask my concern.

'Oh, the usual 50 per cent I believe.' I winced.

'We should get a mixed bag of winners though – I have asked them to send me one of each number,' he said, trailing the remark away.

'One of each number, one of each number!' Did I hear that right? I played it back in my head, then smiled. Suddenly, I felt like someone who had just been given the answers before a quiz night.

As the evening went on, the crowd became increasingly noisy, their horses being projected onto a six-foot screen, to a chorus of shouts, groans and cheers. After five races, having thrown away a few nominal bets, for charity you understand, I noted that the winning numbers thus far had been 2 – 4 – 5 – 7 and 8.

'Time to have a bet,' I thought.

I had the choice of the three numbers yet to win, 1, 3 and 6. And rather than guess which it would be, I backed them all for a fiver each.

Soon, Cliff leapt into action with – 'No more bets – lights out – roll 'em.'

'I think I'll enjoy this,' I mused.

But after two furlongs, at Goodwood, I think, calamity struck – the film broke.

'Lights please – John, have you got that film cement handy?' Cliff made efforts to sound calm and in control, but knocked his drink for six in his anxiety.

After a very long five minutes and a great deal of heckling, John finally did the trick. Suddenly, the lights were dimmed and the race repeated, however, this time without sound.

'Turn it up, John,' a chorus of punters yelled, but it made no difference, and strangely, an equal number found the lack of sound amusing. As it turned out, so did I – 'Winner number 6 pays £5.50 for a £1 stake.'

The next race, we were told, would be a jump race. I supported numbers 1 and 3, hoping that my inside information would see me through.

A jump race it was, although it was the projector that did most of the jumping. It was suggested that the usual camera man's excuse of a 'hair in the gate' should now be 'twigs in the gate'. However, we got there in the end, although the natives were slightly more restive this time, repeatedly chanting, 'What a load of rubbish'.

Sure enough, number 3 won in style. 'I should be enjoying this,' I thought, but somehow, I wasn't.

A 20-minute interval followed for raffle tickets and fish and chips – 'All very civilised,' I told Cliff.

Pat and I enjoyed the supper, while the projectionist, John, played about with the last reel of film.

'Fingers crossed,' I thought, 'this should be number 1.'

Eventually, Cliff stood up with the microphone and told everyone this was to be the last race: by way of a change, an eight-dog race from a track in Florida. 'And,' he continued, steadying his grip on the microphone, 'afterwards, there will be the auction of 50 top quality items – theatre tickets, a case of red wine, an Arsenal signed football and more – the proceeds going to assist school funds, perhaps for some cricket nets, or gym equipment?'

We put our bets on, the lights were lowered, then action!

Oddly, the film started with the presentation of the trophy, followed by the race, run backwards, until all the dogs were safely re-housed in their traps.

I guess John must have somehow rewound it onto another spool, back to front. So now, to test the patience of the most tolerant and, in order to confirm the result, the film was rewound and shown again.

Number 1 still won of course, but unknown to me, a noisy crowd on one of the long tables had been doubling up their stakes on 'Horse number 1,' thereby catastrophically affecting the winning dividend. And so, the very popular result, which paid less than even money, led to a pay-out queue that reached to the back of the hall.

After an interval, with everyone re-seated, the auction began, comically, I thought, with two smart umbrellas from Marks & Spencer's, accompanied by a challenging voice from the back, who claimed to have left them in the cloakroom last term.

By now, everyone apart from John, who was meticulously repacking the spools of film, seemed to be enjoying themselves. In the meantime, I had promised Pat to plough back my ill-gotten gains into the auction if something interesting came up.

It did, and we won a large fresh salmon, flown in from British Columbia; a half-size cricket bat signed by the entire Surrey squad; a hovercraft ferry trip for two from Dover to Calais, which we later discovered was in November and needless to say, never used. Oh, and some Royal Court Theatre tickets to a play that the critics had called 'mentally challenging'.

The school, we heard, had a record-breaking night, vowing to 'do it all again next year'. However, the following day, Pat could not locate her weekly shopping – hurriedly boxed up at Waitrose and put onto the backseat of our car.

Foolishly, in order to take four bottles of wine into the school, I had lifted the box out on to the ground and on being distracted, well that's my excuse, got into the car on the other side.

'How could you be so stupid?' was a phrase I heard repeatedly over the next few days.

However, our neighbour, Cliff, assisted in solving the mystery when later he gave us a list of the auction sales. I scanned the items until seeing: Lot number 51, additional item – assorted groceries – £95.

When all was said and done, I had to admit that whatever advantage I had gained at the Race-Nite I had left behind in the car park.

You win some, you lose some.

*Pat with Busted Luck at Geoff Lewis's yard, Epsom*

*Michael with Red Rum in Woking*

# CHAPTER EIGHTEEN

## *Red Dog on a Cheltenham Special*

Boarding the train at Paddington, there were *Racing Posts* as far as the eye could see. This was mid-March, and to racing people, that means Cheltenham.

Today, Gold Cup day, was the high spot of the jumps season and brought together enthusiasts from all over Britain and Ireland.

If you are travelling to Cheltenham from Greater London, particularly if you like a drink – it is difficult to find anyone today who doesn't – the best way is by train. The choice is yours – Pullman specials, fast trains, slow trains, some with even one or two changes, depending on your pocket, when you want to get there and when you feel capable of getting back.

This train, a Pullman special, is catering for punters who want a little luxury. In fact, we had only travelled a mile before waiters, swaying with trays, posed the question, 'Buck's Fizz or Champagne, Sir?'

Sinking back into my seat, a sigh of relief was in order, having got up at dawn, made the connections from Woking station and then finally, meeting up with Holly on Paddington station.

Holly was a blonde of indeterminate age who I occasionally met up with on big race days. Loosely speaking, she floated between the racing and theatrical circles, although, it must be said, she was a bit of a mystery. However, one thing she told me that I liked to believe was that she was born on Christmas Day from Quaker parents.

Thirty minutes into the trip and the mobiles are out, taking early prices on the Pricewise selections; meanwhile, a dedicated few had brought along laptops for a wider range of punting.

'Full English breakfast Madam, or kippers?'

Holly was asked to make her first selection of the day.

'Eggs, bacon and toast, please. No sausages or black pudding. I think it's a little early for that, don't you?'

She raised a quizzical eyebrow at the waiter, who looked a little unsure. Then, he looked to me, 'And you, Sir?'

'I'll have what she's having,' seemed a good snap decision as we glanced across at our fellow passengers, making contact with nods and smiles.

Whilst waiting for our breakfast I scanned the papers. This year's Gold Cup looked a fascinating puzzle, and although there were 18 runners, the betting centred on four: Looks Like Trouble, a previous Gold Cup winner; Bacchanal, the Aon Chase winner; Willie Mullins' Florida Pearl; and Henrietta Knight's Best Mate, second to Florida Pearl in the King George – try sorting that one out!

Meanwhile, the couple opposite had been very quiet, studying their Timeform racecards with a purposeful intensity. But later, after breakfast and relaxing with a bottle of Chardonnay, they began to chat.

Alan, an accountant, belonged to a couple of small syndicates with shares in horses, while his wife, Maggie, who ran a small hotel in south-west London, confessed she rarely had a holiday, and an occasional trip to the races was her only escape from the job.

She went on to tell us that her son Daniel and his friend were on the same train. He worked in the City and then spent every evening playing poker on the internet. I looked into her eyes – I had to, her mouth was moving too quick and too close for comfort. Was she telling me with pride, or was she worried about her son, like any other mother?

In contrast, Alan opened up to Holly, telling her of his imminent hernia operation before their intended retirement to Spain. 'The trouble is,' he said, turning to me and shifting in his seat with a wince, 'we will have to put our dog, Slippers, into quarantine.'

'Oh dear,' I sympathised, while thinking, 'Bloody hell, I've come out for a day's racing and this is like listening to an episode of 'The Archers'.

Moving along the train in search of the Gents, I saw one or two familiar racegoers; Shoeless Roger, who broke off from his pair of kippers to give me the short history of his verruca, and then further along, Mad Maurice, who told me of a whisper for Last Option in the Foxhunters' Chase.

A card school was in progress near the lavatories; two older men and two youngsters; it looked like a form of poker and a very genial one if the laughter was anything to go by. Anyway, back to Holly, before the train pulled into Cheltenham Spa.

'Where have you been?' Holly had a point. I apologised and was then informed we were going to meet up with Alan and Maggie in the Marquee after the Gold Cup – great, I don't think.

The coach from the station to the racecourse was crawling, due to the traffic; in fact, during the last half-mile people were jumping off to walk the final furlong or two.

Once through the turnstile, an atmosphere of expectancy rushed to meet us, quickly followed by distractions in all directions. Sidetracked by the shops and stalls selling clothing, jewellery, prints and books, Holly was lured further and further from the purpose of our visit, until unbelievably, we missed the first race – the Triumph Hurdle.

However, it turned out to be a blessing, as Charlie Swan, we were told, cleared away on Scolardy, winning by a country mile at 16-1.

Sneaking back past The Guinness Village enclosure, we observed it even more raucous than before, with virtually every inhabitant deep into joyous celebrations.

Part of the skill required to enjoy Cheltenham to the full is in finding the shortest queue to the bar doubled with remembering the route to the nearest lavatory. And with that accomplished, we set off for the paddock to glimpse the runners – 16 of them – for the Stayers' Hurdle, in reality a two-horse race.

On a day like today, finding a short Tote queue is akin to a miracle, but like a miracle, we found one. So, rather than risk the helter-skelter down in the ring, Holly and I put our 'ponies' together and plumped for Baracouda, trusting that Thierry Doumen would time it right; although, having made the bet, I suddenly remembered how often he didn't.

The only serious opposition was Bannow Bay, ridden by the in-form Charlie Swan, with half of Ireland and the entire Guinness Village playing up their winnings.

Over the last, and the bookies were forced to grit their teeth when the champions of Ireland and France battled it out, a dozen lengths clear of the field, until, engulfed in a torrent of sound, the better-backed Baracouda held on to win by a neck.

After long queues at the payout windows, we pushed our returns deep into our pockets and made for the terraces in the hope of getting a good view of the Gold Cup. Holly and I had taken prices on the train to give us a bit more time, her going ambitiously for Alexander Banquet and What's Up Boys and me for old favourites Marlborough and Looks Like Trouble. However, all to no avail, as the young upstart Best Mate stormed past the stands to land the spoils at 7-1, looking like a horse to follow.

Entering the Marquee, we saw Alan and Maggie, queuing for coffee and sandwiches. Luckily, we found a place to sit close by and heard an account of their day. Maggie had bought a gold bracelet and Alan, whilst following her round the stalls, had missed two winners, so he said!

Suddenly, there was a lot of shouting – 'Must be another race,' said Holly.

I scanned the paper, 'The Foxhunters',' I exclaimed, looking up.

Alan went over to see, and came back smiling.

'Did you back the winner?' enquired Maggie.

'No, missed a loser for once,' replied Alan, looking complacent.

'What won it then?' I enquired.

'A longshot, ridden by a Mrs someone or other,' his voice trailing away.

'That's nice,' said Maggie. 'Shows the gals can do it.'

It wasn't until we were leaving the Marquee, to go back to the racecourse, that I looked at the TV screens for the Foxhunters' Chase result.

'Last Option, Last bloody Option; Tote Win £32.90. Would you believe it?' It was the horse Mad Maurice had told me about on the train this morning.

'He'll be unbearable on the way back,' I thought, 'And so might I?'

As the afternoon went on, so our pace slackened, particularly after two more losers. But, just as the afternoon was drawing in, it was suddenly lit up by the popular grey Rooster Booster, who, winning at 8-1, not only replenished our pockets, but sent Holly off for a last look at the shops.

With darkness creeping in and the crowds drifting home, Holly emerged with an assortment of souvenirs including a framed print of Arkle and a luxury pencil box for her daughter.

There were still long queues for the coaches laid on to take us back to the railway station, which, as it turned out, gave us time to join the right one.

On being shepherded to our platform, we were informed that our train was not due for another hour, so we had the choice of either crossing back to the station bar or to the pub around the corner. We chose the latter.

'Churchy me boy, did I tell you about that horse I was given?' The short stocky figure of Mad Maurice blocked my path to the bar.

'Err,' I slowly responded, a better choice I thought than claiming Alzheimer's.

'I've a little party going over in the corner, come and join us and your lady friend too, what's her name?'

'Holly, it's Holly,' I repeated, over the growing swell of conversation. Charming at best, Maurice latched on to Holly while telling her of his stable connections, admiring her print of Arkle and revelling in his timely good fortune.

The pub was by now heaving with racegoers exchanging stories of their shrewd punts and some of the ones that got away.

Maurice's party did justice to his hospitality, and I must admit that Holly and I enjoyed his champagne. However, with time ticking on we returned to the platform in a mellow mood.

Boarding the train, we met up again with Alan and Maggie, who after enjoying with us a much-needed roast dinner and being under the impression we had had a successful day, suggested a game of cards to while away the remainder of the train journey. Nothing unusual today, as one or two schools had already kicked off with poker, brag and even whist.

'I'll see if Daniel brought a spare pack,' said Maggie, springing into action. Five minutes later, she returned brandishing a new pack, still in the original cellophane. I was impressed.

'Now, what would you like to play?' she enquired, first looking at Holly and then me.

Pontoon and then Draw Poker proved a little dull with only four players, so after a while, I suggested: 'Let's play Red Dog. It's known in America as Between the Sheets and that describes it perfectly. It's a very simple three-card game, in which each player in turn is dealt two cards face up, and can bet at evens to any amount in the pot that the third card will fall numerically between the other two. Oh, and the deal passes left after every round.'

'Is that it?' said Maggie.

'Well not quite,' I replied. 'What little skill you need is in varying your stake to your chance of winning. I'll tell you what, let's have a couple of dummy rounds and then what say we start the anti with a quid each in the kitty?'

'Sounds fine by me,' said Alan. 'I've an idea I've played something like this before, I think they called it Shoot or something?'

'Come on then, let's get started,' urged Maggie. So we did.

At first, there were no big gaps between the sheets laid out: 2 and 7; 8 and a Jack, that sort of thing. Then, after about 20 minutes, with the kitty building up nicely, Maggie dealt a 2 and a Queen to Holly.

'That's very good,' said Maggie.

'Yes. An exceptional chance,' affirmed Alan.

'Go on Holly, go the whole kitty,' I encouraged. We quickly assessed the pot at around £110. Holly hesitated for a while and then produced the readies, flinging them into the middle.

Maggie turned over the third card – another Queen – 'Oh, tough luck Holly,' sympathised Alan. 'What a shame,' added Maggie.

I sat there stunned; had I seen it right? Did the Queen of Diamonds come off the bottom?

Nevertheless, from then on, every time it came to Maggie to deal, whatever else was going on in the carriage, and at times, it got very rowdy, I watched her intently.

Strangely, nothing happened. Kitty's came and went, although Maggie did pick up the £220 pot I felt Holly should have had, but that was when I was dealing!

However, much later, about an hour later, with the train only ten minutes out of Paddington, and with £250 in the pot, Maggie dealt Alan a four and an Ace.

Shouts of encouragement came from every quarter, all entreating Alan to 'bet the lot'. On hearing the excitement, Maggie's son Daniel and his friend George had come over, having apparently cleaned out the older men at poker.

A hush came over the table as Maggie dealt the third card.

'Queen of Diamonds,' she announced with a tinge of pride and then congratulated Alan, triumphantly. In a flash, I heard my voice boldly announcing, 'You took that card from the bottom Maggie.'

There was an awkward silence; first everyone looked at me and then, at Maggie. But I kept going. 'You did the same thing earlier,' I said, 'I had to let it go then, because I wasn't 100 per cent sure, but now, you've done it again, and with the very same card.'

Maggie remained silent, but, after an embarrassing pause that seemed an eternity, Daniel said firmly, 'You can't be sure of that Michael. I think you owe my mother an apology.'

At that time, Alan pushed the £250 kitty back across the table and diplomatically suggested, 'Look, let's not spoil a wonderful day out. I suggest we divide the kitty between us. We're coming into Paddington now anyway.'

He had a point, and strangely, it seemed, I had now become the villain.

Maggie hastily got up to leave, excusing herself for a last comfort break.

Then, as she did so, another Queen of Diamonds fell from her lap.

Before going our separate ways from Paddington, Holly and I both said we needed a drink. It was late, but there was a pub open near the station. Finding a table near an old jukebox, we relived the final moments of our journey.

'So what do you think of Red Dog then Holly,' I said.

She shook her head. 'I can't really take it all in; I wonder if they were all in it together?'

It was hard to tell. Holly drank her vodka.

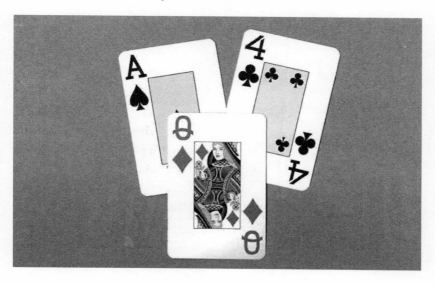

'I never saw Maggie make the switch,' she added, wide-eyed.

'What's that on the jukebox?' I asked, adding, 'Sounds like an old Eagles number.'

'Do you like the Eagles?' she enquired.

'Listen, its *Desperado*,' I replied, intently.

The song continued: 'Don't you try the Queen of Diamonds boy; she'll beat you if she's able. The Queen of Hearts is always your best bet.'

# CHAPTER NINETEEN

## *Hot to Trot*

'Goddamn it, I've got to get a bet down.' Hardly words you would expect from a Canadian on home soil. For this is a country, populated in the main by mild-mannered citizens, occasionally stirred by the rarity of two Canadian ice hockey teams playing each other in the Stanley Cup final. However, underneath their calm exterior lies a passion for harness racing, or trotting as it's often called.

Canada boasts 34 trotting tracks; 16 in the state of Ontario and so, having close relatives in Ottawa, our two-week stay would not be complete without a visit to the Rideau-Carleton Raceway.

My brother-in-law Reg, the most amiable and easygoing guy you could hope to meet, obliged by driving Pat and I, his wife Connie and their new neighbours Alex and Val, the 20 miles to the track.

Throughout the journey, Alex kept us entertained by relentlessly recounting every detail of his youthful rodeo exploits – so much so, the track made an even more welcome sight than usual.

However, on arrival, we quickly settled in the 650-seat dining room overlooking the five-furlong circuit. Apparently, the recent surge of business and the impressive upgrading of the facilities were down to the opening of their casino below the restaurant – 1,250 slot machines and blackjack tables to boot.

Racing apart, which held various degrees of attraction to our party, we quickly joined the queue for the 'all-you-can-eat 100-item buffet', at C$19.99, or ten quid each, if you were working in English.

Reg, who had previous form here, advised us, 'There's no hurry folks. The restaurant is open till late and you can keep coming back for more between the races.' A useful suggestion, I thought, prompting us to lighten our selections from our already overcrowded trays.

In time, when everyone had had their fill, our minds turned to the 14-race programme – nine events for pacers and five for trotters all races run over one mile.

For the uninitiated, a pacer's gait is with the right front and right hind together, followed by their left front and left hind, whereas a trotter's legs move in diagonal pairs – right front with left hind, then left front and right hind. Pacing horses are faster than trotters and to assist their rhythm, they wear straps (hobbles), connecting the legs on each side of the horse. The main benefit being, unlike trotters, they are less likely to break stride.

Our company were, of course, aware of this, but they did have trouble with the intricacies of the form – beautifully laid out to my mind in the style of an enlarged greyhound programme with ten lines of form for each runner.

I thought my answers to our party's questions on the various racecard hieroglyphics would help, but, after none at our table had come close to backing a winner, they reverted to betting on nice names, lucky numbers and some other obscurities.

Punting morale continued to decline, until just before the tenth race – a 'Happy 50th Birthday Fred' type event, worth C$10,000 – the evening's top contest.

Here, for once, every member of our party had picked the same horse, but from different criteria: a good looking black horse; won last time out; lucky number 5; jockey wearing red and white silks; most valuable claimer; and with a memorable name – Black Baby Bunting.

We chose Alex to carry out our commission and he trooped off to the Tote with our C$50 win and place. Meanwhile, eight pacers went to post.

Minutes later, the motorized starting gate moved into action, the sulkies getting in line behind the outstretched wings of the gate, until, on reaching the start, the wings folded up, the vehicle accelerated away and the race was on.

For once there was a buzz around our table – all of us having backed the same horse brought the race into focus.

Due to the small, tight track it was vital to get a good position at the first bend. From there, the drivers formed two lines, one on the rail and the other on the outside. When they passed us, Black Baby

Bunting raced with cover on the outside – fourth spot.

The commentary filtered through the noise and excitement. 'Down the back straight, Altercation leads on the inside, Rose Marie is first over, with Romancing Rita in the pocket and D Jays Doll looking trapped in the death hole.'

'Where's our baby?' wailed Valerie.

'He's still there,' I shouted back over the noise. 'See, on the outside, black saddlecloth, number 5.' But by then, she had scurried off to the nearest TV monitor for a better view.

'At the final bend, Romancing Rita takes it up; Black Baby Bunting pulls out wide to make his run and D Jays Doll descends from the clouds – it's going to be a three-way go.'

We all stood up as the sulkies shot past us, although standing 30 yards before the line it was impossible to judge the result. However, the PA system quickly informed us: 'Attention please, attention please; the judge has called for a print to determine the first three placings.'

Valerie returned from the TV monitor. 'It's so close I can't be sure, but we might have won it.' She was right.

It's always nice to have a winner, but it was really great to share it with the whole table. Alex returned with our winnings, excitedly explaining, 'Here, I've got the girl to write it down: C$8.40 a win and C$3.60 a place – the place is for first and second only.'

'Never mind that,' chipped in Connie, 'How much have we got?'

'In total,' Alex paused for effect, 'C$600.'

It took a further five minutes to sort out who had won what. In fact Alex had to go back to split a C$100 bill into fives and tens to give everyone the right money.

Reg and Connie seemed very happy that everyone else was happy, Connie saying that she was going to play up her luck on the one-armed bandits, even if overall, she couldn't be sure if she was winning or losing. Val said she would go with her, but at this point, the men decided it was high time for a good drink – mainly large gin and tonics.

An hour later, Pat and I went down to see how Connie and Valerie were doing. Connie was known to be an avid slot player, so we patrolled the seemingly endless rows of machines, the sound of their tuneless jingles mixing with the occasional crash of coins downloading into the trays beneath.

Pat spotted them first, but there seemed to be some sort of trouble. Valerie looked upset and was talking to a member of the security staff – we stood by and listened in.

'I had been playing the quarter machines further down the row, but not having much luck came up here to play the dollar slots. After a while, I won a 20 and then a 50. Then a lady came up, bumped into me and dropped her handbag – the contents went all over the floor, so I helped her pick them up. She thanked me and then carried on. But, when I started to play again, I noticed there were hardly any coins in my bucket; it had been at least half-full. Somehow, I think she must have made a switch, perhaps with the help of an accomplice, but Connie didn't see it and neither did I.'

The security officer said he had come across a similar type of hustle once before. 'It was a pity there were no witnesses,' he said. Nevertheless, he took a description of the suspect and then Valerie's name, address and phone number. 'We will be in touch Madam.'

In the aftermath, Valerie and Connie both declared, 'That's it for me; I'll never touch another one-armed bandit ever again.'

The day before we returned to England, Reg and Connie booked for us to have a farewell meal in a reputable steak house. Their three daughters – Pat, Jackie and Debi, complete with husbands and families, would make it a family night out. Alex and Valerie were also coming.

As so often happens at the end of an evening, beer followed beer and gin followed gin. Alex, whom I had the pleasure of sitting next to, resumed his rodeo tales of derring-do.

He had ridden until his age, 42, and a broken leg finally forced him to quit. However, tonight, he was reliving the best of it.

'You've no idea what it's like Michael, man verses beast, it's very basic, primitive almost.'

Then calling for everyone's attention, he quizzed me with the following:

'I bet you have never ridden a beast of any description.'

'Oh I wouldn't say that, let me think,' I said, hesitantly.

'No, come on, of course you haven't,' he said forcefully, the gin beginning to get the upper hand.

'I'll bet you C$50,' he said, pulling some notes from his jacket pocket. 'No look, see here, make it 60, if you can prove that you have.'

'OK,' I said, not wishing to be bullied and having the vague recollection of an old snap of me riding a white horse on Swansea sands. And so, with a show of confidence that I did not feel, I slapped my C$60 on the table and went out to the front of the steakhouse for a breath of much-needed air.

And there it stood – a larger than life-size model of a young prize bull.

Boosted by more than a few gins, I took what I saw as a heaven-sent opportunity. So just as Pat and Debi were coming to take me back, I clambered aboard the bull and posed as if riding in a rodeo.

Debi had her mobile phone with her and took the photo. Chased back inside by an arm-waving security guard, I fled through the entrance lobby, passing two jackpot slots, en route to our party.

Debi mischievously made a beeline for Alex.

'I think you've lost your bet,' she said provokingly.

'How's that?' Alex slurred.

She showed him the picture.

'Why, that son of a bitch,' he moaned. 'I've been set up,' he added, too drunk to realise he was looking at a model.

We let him pay out and then, a few minutes later, I did the decent thing and gave the dollars back to Valerie.

As if on cue, while going to the bar for drinks, less than ten minutes later I caught sight of Val, accompanied by Connie, gleefully tottering off to the lobby slot machines clutching her dollars.

# CHAPTER TWENTY

## *Heads You Lose*

Over the years, having acquired a small collection of bronze resin sculptures – minor trophies won by a few good Open race greyhounds – I had always wanted to own a solid bronze original sculpture of a greyhound. Until now this had always seemed a luxury I would have difficulty in justifying to the family. But then, one night while looking at eBay and on entering the word greyhound in the search box, I was surprised to see for sale, 'Bronze sculpture of Racing Greyhounds heads – Stunning'. I was stunned and clicked on the box saying 'Watch this item'.

Over the next few days, I returned to view the sculpture many times, whilst the vendor, although without provenance, assured me that the sculpture was genuine, solid bronze with a green patina, and weighed 12 kilograms.

So, with little time of the auction remaining and the bidding going up, I put in a last-minute maximum bid of £180. Surprised and delighted, I won the piece for £161 plus postage. Unfortunately, that wasn't the end of it. In fact, it was just the beginning, for having sent off my cheque and waited for news of the sculpture's despatch, I received no response – not then, or in two weeks' time, or in six weeks' time.

Meanwhile, having looked at the vendor's feedback page, I was among a dozen or so similarly disappointed buyers of quality goods. At this point, I telephoned my bank to see if the cheque had been cashed – amazingly, it hadn't, so the bank agreed to stop the cheque. Furthermore, after reading that other buyers were intent on contacting the police, it was clear that the bird had flown.

Surprisingly, a week later, there appeared on eBay from a London bookseller: 'Greyhound pair bronze dog heads by M Bertin – Art Deco – starting price £600'. Since the picture of the greyhound heads looked identical to the one I had attempted to buy, I emailed the new vendor with the details of my failed purchase and asked him to ring me, in an attempt to clear up the mystery. He did, at midnight.

His response was hostile: 'This sculpture has got nothing to do with you. I bought it from a back-street auction house in London.'

'Did you obtain any provenance?' I enquired.

'None whatsoever,' he replied defiantly. 'But I do know the work of the artist. He's a Frenchman, who made bronze reliefs of motorcyclists and fashionable car mascots, that sort of thing, all in the art deco style of the 1920-30s.'

After a while, when he realised I wasn't accusing him of anything and just seeking his advice, he became more friendly and when it turned out he used to be a greyhound racing enthusiast and inveterate racegoer, and learned of my connections with both sports, John and I chatted on into the early hours.

'This has all the intrigue of a Dick Francis novel,' he said. 'I'll keep you posted if I find out anymore.'

The next day he sent me details of the website Artnet, which showed sales of a similar sculpture in 1996, and more recently in 2006, when at Christie's, the bronze, not numbered, sold for £600. However, John's statue failed to sell and when he put it up on eBay for a further ten days, it failed again.

Within a period of six weeks, two further sculptures appeared on eBay, both with identical descriptions, these at a more modest £350; however, neither sold despite repeated attempts.

I tried to reason that if all were genuine, Bertin must have produced an edition of say, a dozen, and unbelievably these had all come on the market at the same time, more than 75 years after the original. On reflection, it was unbelievable.

Strangely, the auction title of the work was always, either 'The finish line', or 'At the finishing line', yet without muzzles these dogs appeared to be coursing greyhounds – no finishing line there.

At this point, the chain of events took an unexpected twist. An old racing friend, Leonard Boss, telephoned to say he had just bought a bronze sculpture of a pair of greyhounds for £500. His description sounded familiar and when he brought it round to show me and I told him of my experience, we both had a good laugh.

Lennie then told me he was taking his wife to Egypt for a couple of months and sportingly suggested, in view of my disappointment, that I could keep the sculpture at my place until he returned. He did, however, ask as a favour that I check his post once a week and send on anything that looked important. He gave me a spare key, we shook hands and spoke of a dinner when he returned.

Things went on as usual, until two weeks later, when late that Saturday night there was a heavy knock on the front door. Looking out from the dining room, I could see two shadowy figures, one swaying a little. I put on the outside light and vaguely recognised one of the men as a rather dodgy Wimbledon dog man I used to have dealings with. I opened the door.

'Churchy, you old dog; you're still here? I remember your parties.'

'Harry, isn't it?' I asked. 'Yes, and this is Bob,' he replied.

We shook hands and I offered them a drink.

After recalling when we last met each other, Harry said, 'We've just come from Wimbledon.'

'Good night?' I enquired.

'A very good night,' he said triumphantly. 'Backed trap one in the big race, backed it twice actually – won £850. The red dog's were good to me tonight.'

'Yeah, I had a bit on too,' added Bob.

Just then, Harry caught sight of the bronze sculpture in the corner of the room.

'Cor, that looks a nice piece of bronze. Where did you get that?'

'A friend gave it to me,' I said and for some reason I left out 'to mind', quietly adding, 'for looking after his house.'

'It looks brilliant, don't it Bob?' Bob nodded in agreement. 'What would you pay for something like that?' Harry asked, unabashed.

'Don't know for sure,' I responded. 'About £500 – £600, something like that, I imagine.' Harry paused and then said, 'Can I have another beer, Churchy?'

After changing the subject to where he was working, he came back to ask, 'I know it's a bit of a cheek and that, but would you be willing to sell the bronze, say for £650?'

'No I couldn't,' I said, 'you see . . .'

'£700 then,' Harry pressed.

Suddenly, I was tempted. I was certain I could get another sculpture like this for less, replace Lennie's bronze and then share the profit with him. It was madness really, but it made sense financially.

'OK then, for cash.'

He pulled out a wad of notes, and counted out £700.

'Always wanted a pukka bronze sculpture, and if I don't get this one, I'll probably give it all back to the bookies and have nothing to show for it.'

I could see his logic, but I wondered how I was going to explain this to Lennie if it all backfired.

A minute or two later, Harry and Bob struggled out with the 12 kilo sculpture, under cover of darkness, you could say.

It took about ten days to locate another sculpture, this one, I'm glad to say, for £350. Ironically, that was half of what Harry was determined to pay for it and was set to yield Lennie and I £175 each from the buying and selling.

In the meantime, I had learnt of the 'lost wax method' of reproducing original bronzes. A method that would explain the recent plethora of Bertin bronzes.

The procedure involved the original sculpture, clay, plaster, rubber and hot wax. When the hollow wax mould is removed, it is dipped into a ceramic slurry and then placed in a furnace. Whereupon, the ceramic shell hardens to become the mould, the wax melts and later, molten bronze is poured in. To complete the process, the ceramic is chipped away and the bronze carefully 'finished' with a patina. So there you have it!

On arrival, the new sculpture was satisfyingly displayed in my dining room awaiting Lennie's return.

Strangely, soon after, I received a phone call from a distressed Harry, saying his house had been burgled and the bronze sculpture stolen. Furthermore, could he come around and get some formal receipt, so he could claim on his contents' insurance? Bloody hell! It was then I remembered that Harry's nickname had been 'The Insurance Man'.

My first priority was to get the new sculpture back into Lennie's house as soon as possible. After all, Harry might not be too pleased to see a similar bronze on my table so soon.

That evening, Harry came to the door again.

'Hi Harry; what bad luck.'

'Yeah, tragic mate, I'm really gutted. Still, if you can write me a receipt, make it look formal like – signed and dated – I can claim it back on my insurance.'

'Of course Harry, I just think it's such bad luck. You hadn't had it long. Did you show it off a bit to people?'

'No, kept it on the hall table. It was too bloody heavy to move around.'

Whilst I was getting pen and paper, Harry said, 'You wouldn't do me a favour mate?'

'What's that then?' I said.

'Make it out for a grand, no, say £950, looks better.'

'No I daren't. That would be asking for trouble, anyway, £700 is better, more believable and keeps us both above board.'

Harry shook his head and looked a little thwarted, but we left on good terms.

'See you at the dogs one night Churchy?'

'Yeah, look forward to it,' I said, and watched his car disappear out of the drive.

'Keeps us both above board – above board.' What was I saying. I had sold Lennie's bronze behind his back, gambled on finding a replacement, to make a 100 per cent profit. How was that for 'above board' – I don't think so.

A month later, a car pulled up in the drive. It was Lennie, back from Egypt, with his wife, Belinda, both of them looking seriously suntanned.

'Michael, how are you? Pat, good to see you.'

They came in and made themselves at home.

After a while Lennie said, 'Look, as soon as I've gone through the mail and Belinda's smartened the place up a bit, we would like you to come round for a meal – tell you about our adventures.'

'That will be nice – sounds fun,' I said, adding, 'By the way, when we come round I've got a surprise for you.'


A few days later, we heard of their adventures in the Valley of the Kings, the Sinai desert and on the Nile, accompanied by some very fine brandy.

Later in the evening, his hand rested on his greyhound bronze.

'Thanks for looking after these fellows – nice aren't they? I doubt if it's the original, but at least this one's unique – see, I carved my initials on the base, before we went to Egypt – makes it more personal, don't you think?'

He turned the sculpture around and there, at the back, were his initials L.B.

'Now, about your surprise, Michael?'

# CHAPTER TWENTY-ONE

## *A Derby Day to Remember*

'A perfect ride in a perfect race from the perfect horse,' so said jubilant trainer Peter Chapple-Hyam after Authorized's awesome Derby victory. And on that most glorious sunny day at Epsom, where more than 100,000 racegoers celebrated with Frankie Dettori, none would give him an argument.

The spontaneous joy that cheered Dettori up the straight and into the winner's enclosure was, of course, not mirrored in the bookmakers' faces; some 80 per cent of all bets were on Authorized, including one bet of £500,000, costing them a total of around £50 million.

Whilst it seemed the world rejoiced in Frankie's win at his 15th attempt, to this historian the occasion brought back memories of Sir Gordon Richards' victory in the Coronation Derby of 1953 when, at his 28th and final attempt, he landed the prize on Pinza, before an incredible attendance of 750,000.

At this time, I think it fair to tell you of my affinity with the Derby. Firstly, my mother and father were married on the day Windsor Lad won the Derby in 1934 and I was supposedly conceived a year later, on the night that Bahram won the race!

Whether or not this affected my gene bank, I cannot say, but, having become the unofficial school bookmaker at 11 years old, I proceeded to make certain the pilgrimage to Epsom thereafter. That was until this year.

Gardening, never very high on my list of loves, was this year to disenchant me forever.

An over-zealous attack of patio-laying left me with a trapped nerve at the base of my spine and a crushed nerve below my left knee, the consequence of which threatened to jeopardise a 60-year family tradition of going to the Derby.

Doctors, radiologists and physiotherapists all played their part to alleviate my pain. However, in the lead up to the Derby, the slow progress of my condition caused speculation amongst my nearest and dearest, with comments such as: 'Michael always said, if he wasn't at the Derby he'd be dead!'

Then, five days before the big race, the situation took a turn for the worse. My wife Pat, returning from the supermarket, surprisingly dropped a litre bottle of brandy from chest height onto her big toe, so breaking it, but thankfully, not the bottle. Once again, the medical profession was put to the test. In the meantime, incoming phone calls inquiring of our health became so frequent, that one half expected a progress report at the end of the 'News at Ten' – 'and finally . . .'

Derby Day arrived, firstly for Pat with a trip to the drop-in hospital for a change of dressing – a monster bandage, which would not have looked out of place in a *Beano* comic strip. And so, dosed up with unofficial remedies of five-star brandy and a variety of painkillers, Pat and I arrived at Epsom, in high spirits and in good time. However, on entering the Queen's Stand in a wickedly expensive dress and jacket, rounded off with heavy trekking sandals, Pat drew comments varying from 'Very Zandra Rhodes' to, 'Is that the new dual purpose look?'

Inevitably, after the first race my remedy had worn off and although

Pat's pain management was holding out, I had to return to the car park to recuperate. However, on the premise that you can't keep a good man down, two hours later, suitably refreshed, I returned to the course to join our party in time to see the Derby parade, and joy of joys, to back and see Authorized win a memorable Derby.

At this point, I would usually speed down to the winner's enclosure, in an attempt to pat the winner coming in, and hear the celebratory speeches. It seemed like a 100-1 shot this year.

From the Queen's Stand steppings, adrenaline fuelled my progress, until engulfed by the massive crowd and in danger of falling, I felt an arm on my shoulder. It was *Racing Post* colleague Matt Doyle, known to *At The Races* viewers as 'The Pharoah'. From then on, he guided me through the crowd as if parting the Red Sea, and after a lot of laughter we arrived just in time to nearly pat the winner on the back. Fortunately, we were able to see Frankie's historic dismount at close quarters and heard all the emotional speeches.

Among those standing close by was winning trainer Peter Chapple-Hyam, the 44-year-old son of a Leamington grocer, who, having previously won the Derby with Dr Devious in 1992, later endured a rollercoaster ride that included a sacking from his father-in-law Robert Sangster, and a lean spell of training in Hong Kong. However, today his exuberance knew no bounds and he may go into the record books as the first winning trainer to eat his racecard!

Twenty minutes later, with the runners going down for the next race, Pat and the members of our party greeted me.

'Where have you been and how did you get down to the winner's enclosure?'

I did feel a little irresponsible, but, there again, it was Derby Day, Frankie's day, and for Pat and I and 100,000 other racegoers, it was now to be an unforgettable day.

*Authorized winning the 2007 Derby (© Pat Church)*

*Authorized and Frankie win the 2007 Derby (© Pat Church)*

That evening, sitting at home watching the re-runs of the race and resting our injuries, we both agreed that despite our suffering, it would take more than that to keep us away from going to the Derby.

## And a year later . . .

What a difference in the post-race atmosphere.

This time there was none of the exuberance that greeted Frankie Dettori the year before. In fact, the situation brought to mind the resentment and muted reception received by Lester Piggott when bringing in Roberto in 1972. Piggott had changed his Derby mount many times, before finally taking the ride promised to Bill Williamson three days before the race.

The issue here, however, was with New Approach's trainer Jim Bolger, who having clearly told the press that he preferred his colt to run in the Irish, rather than the English Derby, changed his mind only days before the race to the consternation and criticism of the press and punters alike.

Nevertheless, in defence of both Derby winners, it has to be said that no other jockey than Piggott would have won on Roberto, and without doubt, the manner of New Approach's victory proved him to be a worthy winner of the great race.

A few days after the Derby, I noticed a touching piece by Nancy Sexton in the *Racing Post*.

She related that New Approach had been the final foal out of Park Express and over the previous five years, the mare had slowly become blind. To keep her from fretting about New Approach's whereabouts, he was fitted with a light, leather strap with a bell on it, so that she was always aware of his movements.

In the same article Seamus Burns, whose Lodge Park Stud in Kilkenny bred the Derby winner, stressed the positive side of the situation.

'Tremendous credit has to go to Jim, who has handled the horse brilliantly, and to the ride Kevin Manning gave him at Epsom. And it was great to see how pleased his owners were.'

Now the dust has settled on the whole affair, the words of the Bard seem appropriate – 'All's well that ends well.'

# *INDEX*